GENES AND GENDER

THIRD IN A SERIES
ON HEREDITARIANISM AND WOMEN

Gordian Science Series

Genes and Gender: I
On Hereditarianism and Women

Genes and Gender: II
Pitfalls in Research on Sex and Gender

Genes and Gender: III
Genetic Determinism and Children

GENES AND GENDER: III
GENETIC DETERMINISM AND CHILDREN

Edited by
Ethel Tobach and Betty Rosoff

GORDIAN PRESS
NEW YORK
1980

GORDIAN PRESS, INC.
85 Tompkins Street
Staten Island, NY 10304

First Edition

Copyright © 1980 by
Ethel Tobach and Betty Rosoff

Library of Congress Cataloging in Publication Data

Main entry under title:

Genetic determinism and children.

   (Genes and gender; 3)
    1. Children—Addresses, essays, lectures.
2. Parenting—Addresses, essays, lectures.
3. Heredity—Addresses, essays, lectures. I. Tobach, Ethel. II. Rosoff, Betty. III. Series.
HQ767.9.G46   305.2′3   80-24176
ISBN 0-87752-221-9

CONTENTS

To Charlie and Hy

who epitomize the guys who know
what it is all about
showing by their own activities and support of ours
that it is all about
the struggle for equality, dignity and
the appreciation of human worth

TO THE SCIENTISTS

Phyllis Witte

They can examine a single cell under a microscope, tell you its intricate composition.

They can separate white blood cells from red blood cells.

Little by little they are coming closer toward a cure for cancer and typing all viruses.

They can create a child in a tube, even bring the dead back to life.

But can they eliminate poverty, can they stop pain?

Dear Scientists,

Can you stop human degradation and humiliation?

Can you shorten the unemployment line?

Can you convince the kid on the street corner that the concrete on which he stands is slightly cracked?

Can you give back the sixty years that my father worked to keep a buck in his pocket?

Do you know what the Upper Eastside and Harlem really need?

I am saying that there is a sickness that runs through this society that goes beyond the test tube, beyond the contamination of the cell,

that is beyond the power of the microscope, and all the bright stainless steel instruments that can be invented,

I'm saying, "Do you know what I mean?" I'm saying, can you see the total picture without taking the x-ray?

PROLOGUE

Children are most vulnerable to damaging practices based on biological or genetic determinism (the individual is determined by the genes and nothing can change it). Policies based on genetic determinism result in racist testing which tracks children into inappropriate scholastic settings; decide whether a child should be trained for a job after minimum schooling or be given college preparation; and prescribe a course of study for the child solely on the basis of gender. The children are least prepared for such racist and sexist onslaughts because of inexperience in recognizing and knowing how to combat such attacks.

Children are also left the legacies of the discrimination their parents suffered, and the situations into which they were born subject them to further racism and sexism. It is understandable, therefore, that the speakers at the Third Conference on Genes and Gender, held during the International Year of the Child, found it necessary to talk about these legacies and situations. Children have to be understood in the context of the world in which they live, and in the context of the experiences of the first individuals with which they are socialized: the parents. The spiraling interconnectedness of historical, economic, physiological and psychological processes produces parents and children.

One could start at any point in that continuous spiral called human parenting and childhood. Mullings starts us off on that spiraling path with her analyses of the fundamental cultural and historical processes which socialize women and men.

Balk's discussion of bonding between mother and child demonstrates the invalidity of applying instinct theory to obstetric practice. Vroman's paper presents the underlying biological, racist and sexist bias of the medical model in delivery of health care. The reports by Rodriguez and López detail the racist, sexist and class forces which determine whether a child ever becomes a reality. Gelles' presentation of the racist and sexist training of those who are assigned by society to care for the mother and child complements these papers.

The ideology of educational practice similarly reveals their genetic determinist character as expressed in racism and sexism. Schatzkin analyzes the complexity of prenatal stages of development and demonstrates the misuse of science to stigmatize children as uneducable. The personal testimony of Morales and Lovell and the contribution by Burnham underscore the abuse of minority children in our society. John-Steiner and Gordon discuss the pseudoscience of social Darwinism, biological determinism and testers like Arthur Jensen.

A society which teaches and promotes "scientific theories" such as sociobiology, ethology and meritocracy is understandably likely to advertise such ideas in its media as well as in its educational and governmental policies. Browne's analysis of teen-age pregnancy, exposes once again how the victim is blamed and seen as the cause. Her contribution lays the groundwork for the paper by Bartlett, who brings us around to the next level of the spiral, the institution known as "the family". Here once again, the historical, economic, physiological and psychological processes are seen to produce individuals, parents and children who must deal with racism and sexism.

The Conference brought together people who sought solutions to these problems: first, through understanding the theories which are responsible for policies; second, through the exposure of those who use pseudoscience to justify repressive social practices and governmental policies, and those whose conclusions are based on invalid scientific methods and analyses; and third, through sharing knowledge that can be used as weapons in the fight against sexism and racism. Some of those who participated in the Conference were Bea Benkov, J. A. Davidson, Willie Golphin, Cynthia Jenkins, and Alan Jennings, members of Community & Social Agency Employees Union, District Council 1707, AFSCME who also ran the children's day-care center. We thank their President, Bettye Roberts, who brought us together. Many people chaired and acted as discussants in the sessions and contributed their experiences towards our common goals: Judith Bellin; Lenora Bosley; Bill Carlotti; Thelma Dailey; Parimal Das; Barbara Fisher; Ana Flores; Victoria Hashmall Freedman; Denise Fuge; Frances Hubbard; Eleanor Leacock; Lee Lee; Sandra Lee; Ann Okongwu; Connie Pohl and James V. Williams. Others helped in publicizing the Conference and carrying out the many tasks which go into making a Conference possible: Edward H. Elkind; Vickie I; Geraldine Miller; Shiduzie Okongwu; Jorge Perez; Iris Toros; Georgie Weaver; Marcella West; and Eileen Zalisk. We also wish to thank Kate Flores and Shirley Bortoluzzi for their help in editing these proceedings.

Above all, we wish to express our gratitude to our poets who gave an important dimension to our meeting and the proceedings: Linda Dudley and Phyllis Witte.

Betty Rosoff and Ethel Tobach

WOMAN AND MOTHER
IN SOCIETY

Don't Bother to Wait

Phyllis Witte

It is as simple as a conversation on the telephone with Erica.

Erica tells me how a friend of hers couldn't cope with her life anymore, the pressure her friend felt was too much: having a daughter, no husband, not very good at being a mother, what will she do with her own life? She decided to check into a psychiatric hospital for a few days. Later she called Erica. Erica asked her why she couldn't have stayed with her for a few days instead of checking into a hospital. Erica asks me, "Why do people in this society check into mental hospitals when they have difficulties in their lives, why can't they spend some time at the home of a friend?" "When the revolution comes," says Erica over the telephone, "There won't be a need for people to check themselves into hospitals. I wish the revolution would come already, it's too damn long in coming."

Even after the receiver is down her words stay with me, "When the revolution comes." Erica waits for the revolution. How can I explain to Erica that the revolution is having her friend at her home for a few days, that the revolution is my dime in the pay phone to say, "How are you, I miss you," that the revolution is this poem, even after the receiver has been put down.

NOTES ON WOMEN, WORK AND SOCIETY *

Leith Mullings, Ph.D.

Columbia University

This conference, held in honor of the International Year of
the Child, calls on us to struggle against those practices that
result in differential treatment of children according to sex,
race and socioeconomic status, and to promote those that en-
able children to enrich their own lives and our society. One
of the most pernicious theories that has, for centuries, consistently promoted and rationalized the differential access of
human beings to the resources of society is that of genetic
determinism. In its various forms, this view serves to justify
the ranking of people on the basis of class, race, ethnicity and
sex. It suggests that such distinctions have biological implications, determining potential, ability and, ultimately, life
chances. This concept serves to rationalize the sentiment that
categories of people, defined by class, race and gender, are
relegated to certain tasks and socioeconomic levels because
their biological programming limits them to such statuses.

That there are anatomical differences between males and
females is undisputed; what remains very much at issue is the
meaning of this differentiation. In general, genetic determin-
ists have argued that biological differences have "natural"
consequences, that the division of labor—usually some variant
of the home/work, private/public dichotomy, and, indeed, the
inequalities between men and women have a genetic origin
and therefore will persist in some form regardless of the structural arrangements of society. Much of the cross-cultural and
historical data calls such a view into question. In this paper,
I will review some of the evidence which suggests that the

* I would like to thank Jean Carey Bond and Eleanor Leacock for reading
and commenting on this paper.

15

sexual division of labor and the ideology of sex roles are not ultimately determined by biological constraints, but by the structural arrangements of a given society.

Upon examination of the cross-cultural evidence, anthropologists of very different perspectives find that in general, the way in which labor is divided between the sexes is so diverse that it is difficult to correlate the division of tasks with the biological or physical attributes of either sex.[7, 11, 12] We find that assignments vary from one culture to another. Such tasks as agriculture, animal herding, marketing, or the transporting of heavy loads are performed by women in some cultures and by men in others. Whatever the nature of the division of labor, however, the rationale for it is usually biological. For example, the Arapesh say that women have stronger heads than men and it is the women rather than the men who transport heavy loads on their heads. The Kota of India claim that women have stronger heads, but weaker arms; women carry all loads on their heads while men carry the loads in their arms.[7] Even within the same geographical area, neighboring societies may make different assignments of sex-related roles: Navaho women in the southwest United States do the weaving, but among the neighboring Pueblos, weaving is undertaken by the men.[7]

It is not necessary to look to other societies to find that assignment of sex-segregated tasks are more related to the exigencies of historical development than to biological differences. Blau[3] notes that in the sex-segregated United States, the gender composition of occupations is subject to regional variation. For example, in the Midwest cornhuskers are traditionally women, while trimmers are always men; in the Far West, cornhuskers are men and trimmers are women. An occupation that is predominantly female in one industry may be predominantly male in another; thus, in electrical machinery equipment and supplies, the 1960 census reported that 67% of the assemblers were women, while in motor vehicles and motor vehicle equipment only 16% of the assemblers were women.

The correlation between anatomical differences and sex-related tasks, then, is far from clear. Historically, the major

16

exception seems to be hunting, which was thought to be almost universally assigned to men, leading investigators to conclude that the biological fact of women's reproductive capacities constrained their ability to hunt, determining this initial division of labor. Sociobiologists have taken this further to suggest that because the early division of labor revolves around the anatomical difference between males and females, it is likely to persist in all types of societies:

> In hunter-gatherer societies men hunt and women stay home. This strong bias persists in most agricultural and industrial societies, and on that ground alone appears to have a genetic origin. . . . My own guess is that the genetic bias is intense enough to cause a substantial division of labor even in the most free and most egalitarian of future societies . . . even with identical education and equal access to all professions, men are likely to continue to play a disproportionate role in political life, business and science.[21]

Recent evidence calls many of these assumptions into question. In a provocative account of the evolution of the family and women's roles, Lila Liebowitz argues persuasively that the early division of labor was molded by socioeconomic considerations, not by biological imperatives in and of themselves.[12] Greatly simplified, her argument runs as follows: rather than the division of labor whereby men hunt and women gather and care for the children being a "natural" and perpetual outcome of anatomical differences, the sexual division of labor was the result of specific socioecological transformations. It is not the case, as is generally assumed, that women were excluded from all types of hunting.[1] The division of labor was associated with the development of hunting with projectile weapons—pursuing and killing large mobile animals—as opposed to earlier forms of hunting, such as drives, individual hunting of small game or "surround" hunting. It was in the specific conditions where meat became a regular part of the diet and resources were scarce, thus making dispersal into small groups a necessity, that projectile hunting was associated with a sexual division of labor. As the ability to remain inconspicuous and to surprise the animal was key in this type of hunting, small groups became more efficient, as opposed to surround or drive hunting where large groups were required to surround or drive the animal.

It was with the development of these socioecological circumstances, characterized by small groups and projectile hunting, that a woman with children found herself encumbered as a hunter. Nursing children must be fed and young children need constant care. In a small social unit having few nursing mothers and in which a nursing mother could not easily count on another nursing mother for care of her children, the assignment of men to hunt and women to gather and take care of the children becomes predictable, practical and adaptive. Moreover, since men cannot nurse children, the loss of a woman in the relatively dangerous occupation of hunting would have been more serious than the loss of a man. Since effective hunting requires a certain skill acquired through training, differential training and socialization of the sexes established, reinforced and perpetuated this division of labor.

If Liebowitz's assertions are valid, it seems that while anatomical differences determined which sex cared for the children, the necessity for a sexual division of labor arose not from biological or genetic imperatives, but became necessary only as a result of a particular configuration of ecological, economic and historical transformations. Thus, the sexual division of labor might not be "natural" and therefore enduring, but social and subject to change as social arrangements change. Numerous studies have pointed to the impact of such factors as private property, the evolution of the state, and warfare on the status of women, often transforming the division of labor into relationships of domination and subjugation. (For example, see[8, 9, 14, 17])

Although the evidence is not yet all in and reconstruction of earlier epochs must be undertaken with caution, a glance at the history of women's roles in the United States suggests similar conclusions: that it is not biology, but society which

18

ultimately determines the division of labor. The sexual division of labor has not been fixed, but has varied according to historical circumstances, and it has been very different for different classes. During the colonial period, although in England and Europe women were routinely employed as mowers, reapers and haymakers,[3] in the colonies among the non-slave population, agricultural tasks were primarily the domain of men, with women being employed in the household industries, and producing most of the colonies' manufactured goods. As labor shortages increased with the invasion of the frontier, the division of labor was modified to fit the needs of the society. Indeed, the transformation occurred during the journey itself. At the beginning of the westward journey, sex tasks were rigidly segregated; by mid-journey, due to the vicissitudes of the "Trail", most women worked at male tasks.[2] Increasing land shortages in the evolving frontier society found women in a variety of non-traditional occupations, including tavern keepers, traders, printers and publishers, as well as the more traditional domestic ones.[3] Despite the separation between the home and the workplace which industrialization fostered, women played a crucial role in the development of the factory system. With the introduction of the power loom in 1814 and the creation of the textile industry, women—working class women—comprised the bulk of this industrial work force. At various points during the 19th and 20th centuries, labor shortages, fluctuations in demand and technical innovations resulted in a shift toward greater numbers of female employees in such industries as shoe manufacturing, teaching, cigar making and clerical work. It appears that the question of whether or not women were in the home, of what they did or did not do, has been more related to class than to sex, determined by society rather than biology.

The discrepancy between the roles of women of different classes has perhaps been greater than that between men and women of the same class. While femininity was described in terms of non-participation in the labor force, and upper class women were allegedly fainting in parlors, immigrant working class women were laboring 12 hours a day in factories and Afro-American women were toiling for 16 hours or more in the fields. While womanliness was projected as intertwined with homemaking, and although single women comprised the majority of working women, the working wife seems to have been more prevalent than is generally assumed. An annual report of the Massachusetts Bureau of Statistics, cited in the April 1875 *Scientific American* concluded on the basis of visits with 397 families, that in the majority of cases working men did not support their families by their own earnings alone but depended on their wives and children for from one fourth to one third of the family earnings.

Perhaps the most dramatic, and heroic, example of the discrepancy between the ideology which holds that divisions of labor are biologically-rooted, and the actual divisions that the socioeconomic system and the class position determine, is that of Afro-American women. Under conditions of chattel slavery where the goal was the greatest exploitation of labor, while the "flowers of southern womanhood" languished in plantation parlors, Afro-American women often did the same work as men—under conditions that no human being, male or female, should be subjected to.[10] The contradiction between the ideology of "women's place" as determined by their biology and what Afro-American women were actually doing is movingly described in Sojourner Truth's address to the Akron Convention for women's suffrage:

'That man over there says that women need to be helped into carriages, and lifted over ditches, and to have the best place everywhere. Nobody ever helps me into carriages, or over mud-puddles or gives me any best place, and am I not a woman? Look at me! Look at my arm. I have ploughed, and planted, and gathered into barns, and no man could head me! And am I not a woman? I could work as much and eat as much as a man—when I could get it—and bear the lash as well! And am I not a woman? I have bourne thirteen children, and seen them most all sold off to slavery, and when I cried

out with my mother's grief, none but Jesus heard
me! And am I not a woman?[19] [2]

The effects of racism against Afro-American men and women
in the areas of employment and wages, have compelled
Afro-American women, since "emancipation", to work to help
support themselves and their families, and their labor force
participation has always exceeded that of Euro-American
women.[3] Despite the desire of Afro-American married women
to withdraw from the labor force after slavery, large numbers
or rural women were forced to labor, alongside men, as field
hands (relatively few worked as servants or washerwomen—
occupations that were more common among urban Afro-
Americans).[5]

While their long history of labor force participation may
produce more egalitarian arrangements within the household,
Afro-American women remain the most exploited in the public
arena, receiving the lowest returns for the sale of their labor.
The Census Department calculated that in 1973, the median
annual income of minority women was 49.6% that of white
men (as compared to 56.3% for Euro-American women[4]). This
is primarily a result of the disproportionate confinement of
Afro-American and other minority women to the lowest paying sectors of the labor force.[5] The examples of Afro-American and other working class women dramatically demonstrate the discrepancy between their roles as determined by
the division of labor and the ideology that "the woman's place
is in the home".

The relationship between the ideology of the division of
labor—how differential roles of men and women are rationalized and explained—and the way in which these beliefs relate to the actual social relationships deserves much more
elaborate treatment than I am able to undertake here. However, I would like to speculate a bit on how the ideology bears
on the position of Afro-American and other working class
women. We have noted that throughout the history of the
United States, the normative notions of what a woman ought
to be has tended to be a description of what upper class women

were able to be. Rayna Rapp has portrayed the way in which upper class women, who unlike all other women in the society, have no need to work and therefore can present themselves as ideal wives, mothers and representatives of "high culture".[17] These women, who "become symbols of domesticity and of public service", influence our notions of what feminine behavior should be. The ideology of the division of labor, then, is often far removed from the reality of the experience of minority and other working women, yet it remains the cultural ideal, often buttressed by the canons of religion and rationalized as "natural" by the genetic explanations of science.

To bridge the gap between the ideology of sex roles and the real division of labor, between the biological gender of these women and their status as slaves and workers, requires a new ideological twist. In contemporary society, this takes the familiar form of blaming the victim: sex roles ideology is used by apologists for the social system to castigate women workers, and thus rationalize and deepen their oppression. The cynical theoretical circularity of the argument is most evident in the case of Afro-American women. African women, along with men, were captured, torn from their families, and forced into slave labor, without regard for the niceties of gender differentiation. (Of course, the ideological rationale at that time was to limit the definition of what was human—another pinnacle of genetic determinism.) After emancipation, Afro-American women were coerced, by necessity and otherwise, into the labor force. Gutman[5] reports numerous local situations where planters complained about the lack of cheap field labor because women did not want to work and wished to be supported by their husbands. One Louisiana planter instructed that rent be charged to any non-working wives of ex-slaves. Today, the effects of racism—wage and employment discrimination; the high rate of death and disability of Afro-American men as a result of poor health facilities, disproportionate death from war and more dangerous work conditions—as well as many other stressors of poverty, continue to force Afro-American women into the work force. In general, they do not have the option of choosing whether or not they wish to work. These women, who must work to ensure the survival of their families, are then attacked as "matriarchal".[13] Just as the ideology of racism bridges the gap between the folk belief of an open society with equal opportunity and the superexploitation of Afro-American labor, the ideology of the "castrating" Afro-American woman obscures the role of the socioeconomic system in oppressing them and, further, bridges the contradiction between sex role ideology and the actuality of what women in fact do. To the extent that the ideas of the ruling class become the ruling ideas of society, in the same way that the ideology of racism has confused and divided the working class, sex roles ideology penetrates the home and the workplace. In the home, where the wage paid by the employer will not support the subsistence of the family and the woman must work, tensions and strains arise from the inability of both spouses to "live up to" the role model as defined by the ruling class; in the workplace, it divides those who should be united.

It seems clear that the expression of the division of labor, while rationalized in terms of biological, genetic and personality differences, is ultimately determined by social conditions. There is much disagreement among social scientists about which configuration of social processes is most relevant to explicating the status of women, which I will not recount here. (See Amsden[1] for a discussion of the various economic explanations; these models also have their counterparts in the sociology literature.) While the point of production is not the only arena in which the inequality of women is expressed, the division of labor, its establishment and its perpetuation seem to be rooted in the productive processes, as well as in the relationship of the household to the resources of society. With this in mind, I will briefly indicate some of the functions served by the inequality of contemporary U.S. women in the workplace. (See Rapp,[17] for a discussion of the household.)

In a social system based on the accumulation of profit through the exploitation of labor, the sexual division of labor seems to function to strengthen that system and to increase profits. Clearly, sex-segregated occupations and less pay for the same work maximize profits. One well-documented example of this practice in process was the case of American Telephone and Telegraph Company, whose discriminatory practices were investigated by the Equal Employment Opportunity Commission (EEOC). The EEOC report estimates that wage discrimination against women, through which AT&T was able to hold wages down and increase profits, amounted to $422 million a year in 30 metropolitan areas.[16] The widespread nature of such discriminatory practices is indicated in the male/female wage differential; women earn approximately 60% of what men earn.[1]

With the growth of an organized labor movement and labor militancy, where it is not always possible to put short-term profit-maximizing strategies into effect, the existence of components of the labor force that are subject to discriminatory practices may serve other functions. Because marginally and underemployed people have fewer options and a higher rate of unemployment, they constitute a "reserve army of unemployed" who can be utilized to inhibit wages and benefits demands of employed workers. Unemployment among women is 50% higher than among men, with the unemployment rate of minority women in the last quarter of the century averaging 80% above that of Euro-American women.[1] Again the AT&T case illustrates the way in which this process operates. The EEOC report cites an AT&T Vice President Walter Straley's explanation of why, after years of discrimination, AT&T finally hired minority women: "What a telephone company needs to know about its labor market (is) who is available for work paying as little as $4,000 to $5,000 a year. It is therefore just a plain fact in today's world, telephone company wages are more in line with Black expectations—and the tighter the labor market the more this is true."[20] The report analyzes the results of this practice:

> The Operator job is, quite pointedly, a *horrendous* (italics theirs) job. No greater testimony to this fact exists than the unbelievably high rate at which employees bolt from the job. The Bell System's response is amazing: *rather than restructure the job, improve the wages and provide important new avenues for promotion and transfer*—changes which even common

24

sense would suggest—*AT&T has decided to keep the wages depressed and simply hire more and more Black females* (italics mine).

The inevitable effects of these policy decisions are all too obvious. Most of the Blacks in the Bell System will never have a real chance at a good job. The economic realities of the labor market will force large numbers of Blacks to apply for operator jobs. After all, *any* job is better than no job, any job except operator. The realities of the operator job will thus force Blacks to quit as fast as they are forced to apply.[20]

Since a large majority of the employees were white, we can surmise that the ability of AT&T to hire Afro-American workers, and particularly Afro-American women at a lower wage and worse working conditions, because of their lack of options resulting from discrimination, contributed to AT&T's ability to hold down the salary and benefit level of white women workers to the level at which they could hire Afro-American women. Where males and females work at the same job, or where male workers can be replaced by female workers, this process can also be applied to male workers.

The threat of replacement, as well as the characterizations that are components of contemporary sex roles ideology, vaunting men as superior to women, insisting that the woman's place is in the home and that they are taking jobs from men, can be utilized to divide the working class and inhibit the formation of unified working class organizations that could, presumably, struggle more effectively for greater control of the workplace and better conditions for everyone. To make a case for the way in which the sexual inequality of women functions to increase profits does not require a "conspiracy theory". Although "conspiracy" among corporate interests undoubtedly occurs, overt collusion is not a precondition to perceiving their common interests and pursuing similar actions to advance those interests.

It is also possible for workers to perceive their common interests. The extent to which differences between men and women, among ethnic groups and populations, can be utilized to divide them and increase the profits of employers, depends on the extent to which people are organized to prevent it from occurring. Hopefully, the ability of corporations such as AT&T to perpetuate these circumstances will decrease as women are increasingly organized into trade unions and women's groups concerned with advancing the interests of women, in the context of the class struggle and the struggle against racism. It is interesting to note that Afro-American women have frequently assumed leadership roles in such organizing.[4,10,19] Of course, the success of such efforts will depend on the extent to which working people are able to unite in their own interests, across gender lines and race boundaries. It is interesting to note that the necessity for unity was proclaimed by the Colored National Labor Union, when it convened in 1869, in response to the exclusion of Afro-Americans from Euro-American unions. Upholding the rights of women in industry and unions, the Committee on Women's Labor recommended: "profiting by the mistakes heretofore made by our white fellow citizens in admitting women. . . . that women be cordially included in the invitation to further and organize cooperative societies".[4] While "the mistakes" have certainly not by any means been fully corrected, the necessity for unity is increasingly recognized. Most interesting are the scattered incidents where workers have been able to use protective legislation[6] measures designed for women in such a way as to extend them to increase benefits and protection for male workers as well.

In summary, then, it is undisputed that there are anatomical differences between men and women. However, what these differences come to mean, the significance they assume in a given society, appears to be determined not by the nature of the differences themselves, but by the way in which the society is organized. In a society where profit is the driving force, anatomical differences between males and females, like culture history differences between ethnic groups and phenotypic differences between populations, are utilized in such a way as to support that system and maximize profits. Where such differences converge, as in the case of Afro-American women, oppression will be particularly intense.[15]

Policy implications, then, must relate to changing the basic structure of the socioeconomic system. While all forms of gender asymmetry will not disappear once the social system ceases to be organized around profit, this seems to be the first step in creating the foundation for change. Explanations that do not account for the role of the social system in determining the division of labor, whether they attribute sexual inequality to the anatomy of women or to the congenital dispositions of men, ultimately function to assist in reproducing the socioeconomic system that so defines the division of labor, and divides the people who are oppressed by it. If gender inequality is socially, not naturally, determined the first step in eradicating inequality is addressing the system that profits from it—putting people before profits. Because the destinies of working people, men and women, are economically, politically and socially inextricably linked, this requires the unity of all working people and oppressed minorities, men and women, to create a better world for all our children.

NOTES

(1) I would like to thank Eleanor Leacock for pointing out that the "exclusion" of women from hunting large game among gathering-hunting populations is a popular, but undocumented, stereotype. She notes that although men do most of the hunting, data on the Inuit and native Americans of the Canadian subarctic and for some Australian groups, indicate that women hunt large game when they need or want to.

(2) This was originally recorded at the Akron Convention of the Women's suffrage movement where Sojourner Truth said these words. I have taken the liberty of using "standard" English.

(3) In 1890 the labor force participation for white women was 16.3% compared to 39.7% for non-white women; however, the labor force participation rate for married white women was 2.5%, compared to 22.5% for married non-white women.[6] In 1948 31% of all Euro-American women and 45% of all non-white women were in the labor force;[3] by 1973, 3 out of 5 Afro-American women worked for wages or salary as compared to approximately half of Euro-American women.[16] While the differential between Afro-American and Euro-American women has been narrowing in recent years, the difference in the overall impact of the work experience can be understood more accurately if we examine in addition to marital status, the proportion of women working in specific age groups. In the 25–34 year range—the principal childbearing years—there is a sharp decline in the participation in the labor market of Euro-American women, but an increase in Afro-American women's participation; these are the years when the presence of children makes working more difficult, but for some, more necessary. It is in this age range that the excess of Afro-American women over Euro-American women reaches its peak, with 61.1% of Afro-American women working, as compared with 48.6% of Euro-American women.[16]

(4) There has been some confusion about the differential income of Afro-American women that has resulted from comparison of

28

aggregate annual incomes of Euro-American and Afro-American women. Often these statistics, used to suggest that Afro-American women's wages are higher than those of Euro-American women, do not take into consideration the fact that a greater number of Euro-American women are able to afford to work part-time and to find suitable part-time work. In 1973, 35.5% of the number of full-time employed Euro-American women worked part-time by choice as compared to 24.5% of the number of Afro-American women employed full-time.[16]

(5) The U.S. Women's Bureau, in a survey of four states reported that prior to 1929 the Afro-American working woman averaged $300 annually or $6 per week. In 1955, 6 out of 10 Afro-American women worked in domestic and service jobs, with only 20% in industrial sales and office jobs, in which 59% of the Euro-American women were employed.[4] In the last 15 years, the occupational distribution of Afro-American women workers has dramatically changed, with a move away from domestic work and mestic work and a shift into clerical, professional and factory work.[16] However, although there have been gains related to social status, these have not necessarily registered as equivalent economic gains. In 1959, the median earnings of male clerical workers were $4,785; ten years later, the median annual earnings of female clerical workers were $4,232, and of Afro-American female clerical workers $4,152.[16]

(6) The issue of protective legislation is a very complex one. While it is true that protective legislation has been used in some cases to discriminate against women workers, it is also true that some of the measures ensure minimal protection against the hazards of the workplace, and thus offer some protection to women workers. Where women's movements have been dominated by intellectuals, professionals and housewives, the hazards faced by working class women, particularly those in industry, have not been understood nor considered. Where protective legislation is not clearly discriminatory, rather than seek to eliminate those few protective measures against the hazards of the workplace that are in existence, a more useful approach might be to fight to enact those protective measures and to extend them to all workers.

29

REFERENCES

1   Amsden, A., *An Overview of the Economics of Women and Work.*
    New York: Center for the Social Sciences, Columbia University,
    1978.
2   Bernard, J., Historical and Structural Barriers to Occupational
    Desegregation. In *Women and the Workplace,* M. Blaxall and B.
    Reagan, eds. Chicago: University of Chicago Press, 1976
3   Blau, F., The Data on Women Workers, Past, Present and Future.
    In *Women Working,* A. Stromberg and S. Harkess, eds. California:
    Mayfield Publishing Company, 1978.
4   Foner, Philip, *Organized Labor and the Black Worker* 1619–1973.
    New York: International Publishers, 1974.
5   Gutman, Herbert, *The Black Family in Slavery and Freedom.* New
    York: Pantheon Books, 1976.
6   Goldin, Claudia, Female Labor Force Participation: *The Origin
    of Black and White Differences, 1870 and 1880: Journal of Economic
    His:* XXXVII: 87–1977.
7   Hammond, D. and A. Jablow, *Women in Cultures of the World.*
    California: Cummings Publishing Company, 1976.
8   Harris, Marvin, *Cannibals and Kings.* New York: Random House,
    1977.
9   Leacock, E., Women's Studies in Egalitarian Society: Implica-
    tions for Social Evolution. In *Current Anthropology* 19:247–255,
    1978.
10 Lerner, Gerda, *Black Women in White America.* Pantheon Books,
    New York, 1972.
11 Levi-Strauss, Claude, The Family. In *Family in Transition,* A.
    and J. Skolnick, eds. Boston: Little, Brown, 1971.
12 Liebowitz, L., *Females, Males, Families: A Biosocial Approach.*
    Massachusetts: Duxbury Press, 1978.
13 Moynihan, P., Employment, Income & the Ordeal of the Negro
    Family. *Daedalus* 94:745–770, 1965.

14 Mullings, L., Women and Economic Change in Africa. In *Women in Africa*, N. Hafkin and E. Bay, eds. Stanford: Stanford University Press. California, 1976.

15 Mullings, L., Ethnicity and Stratification in the United States. In *Annals of the New York Academy of Sciences* 318:10–22, 1978.

16 Perlo, Victor, *Economics of Racism*. New York: International Publishers, 1975.

17 Rapp, R., Family and Class in Contemporary America. In *Science and Society* XLII:278–300, 1978.

18 Reiter, Rayna Rapp, The Search for Origins: Unraveling the Threads of Gender Hierarchy. In *Critique of Anthropology* 9 & 10: 5–24, 1977.

19 Rossi, A., ed. *The Feminist Papers*. New York: Bantam Books, 1973.

20 U.S. Equal Employment Opportunity Commission, 'A Unique Competence': A Study of Employment Opportunity in the Bell System. In *Congressional Record*, February 17, 1972, pp. E 1260–E 1261.

21 Wilson, E. Human Decency is Animal. In *The New York Times Magazine*, October 12, 1975.

PARENT-CHILD BONDING

Sophie Balk, M.D.

Bronx Municipal Hospital Center and Albert Einstein College of Medicine

Bonding is the attachment formed by the mother or father with the new born infant. In this article the concept of bonding will be critically discussed as it is presented in the book MATERNAL AND INFANT BONDING by Marshall Klaus and John Kennell.[1] Earlier researchers in the field concentrated on the effects of long term maternal separation on the motor, mental and affective development of the child. The main emphasis of this book is on the attachment processes from the point of view of the mother, which the authors say is crucial to the survival and development of the infant. One aspect of its nature is stated by the authors to be expressed in the Russian proverb "You can't pay anyone to do what a mother will do for free".

The authors claim that the bond formed between mother and child in the first days of life is the fundamental one and influences the child's ability to form other relationships in life. In the early 1900's, as a result of the emphasis on infection control in the nursery, deviations from the process of bonding arose. Even now it is apparent that most normal births are accompanied by several days of partial separation from the mother. In premature births there may be a complete separation from the mother for several days to several weeks.

Several principles are enunciated by these authors as crucial components in the attachment process.

1. There is a sensitive period in the first minutes and hours of life during which it is necessary that parent and child have close contact for optimal development of the child.

2. There are species-specific behavioral responses that are peculiar to humans when they are given their infant. This concept is inferred from animal studies.

3. During the bonding process the infant responds to the parent with body and eye movements, supporting the homily that "you can't love a dishrag."

4. Persons who witness a birth become strongly attached to the infant regardless of parenthood.

5. Early events may have long lasting effects on the child; for example, initial anxieties of the mother may adversely shape the later development of the child.

Studies of different animals have shown that specific behavior around the birth process and immediate aftercare of the young is disrupted if the young and mother are separated right after birth. Sometimes maternal rejection of the young occurs depending on the nature and length of the separation. Other studies have shown that nursing females will adopt unfamiliar young. Some studies suggest a possible hormonal component in animal maternal behavior right after parturition due to increased estrogen levels. However, in some species, virgin females and males will exhibit maternal behavior in the presence of new born animals after species "training."

In humans "normal or natural behavior" is difficult to determine because birth is viewed as an illness requiring hospitalization. Until recently there has been little or no participation in the birthing process by the parents. Parents have entered the process with little preparation and at the discretion of the doctors and nurses in the hospital. After birth the child has been whisked away, not been seen by parents for the next few hours and then just brought to the mother at feeding time.

They report home births showed a pattern of interaction only seen in fragments in hospital births. The mother actively participates in the birth process and picks up the baby immediately. There is a striking mood elevation in association with the excitement of those present and everyone is drawn to the infant for prolonged periods. Breastfeeding starts within 5–6 minutes beginning with prolonged licking by the infant. This is contrasted with hospital births under anesthesia where there is decreased perception in both infant and mother and the excitement associated with the birth of the child is postponed. Some further studies of this "sensitive period" suggested that separation during this time right after birth caused a feeling of less competence on the part of the mother in caring for the baby. One study contrasted two groups: one had early extended contact, i.e., one hour in the first two hours and five extra hours in each of the first three days; the other was routine care, i.e., a glimpse at birth, brief contact the first day and brief feeding times for the next two days. After one month, both groups were questioned about their reactions to the babies crying and their reactions to leaving the baby in someone else's care. In addition, their feeding behavior was observed. The early extended contact group showed a greater tendency to pick up a dry, fed baby that was crying than the control group and were less likely to go out and leave their baby in someone else's care. Time spent in feeding was not significantly different between the two groups but the "early extended care" group showed that the mothers fondled the infant more. After one year the "extended care" group spent more time soothing the infant when crying and assisting the doctor. At two years the linguistic behavior of the mothers when talking to the children in the early extended care group showed more speaking, greater variety of words, more adjectives and fewer commands. At five years this experimental group showed higher IQ's than controls.

Two other studies were reported by the authors. One was performed in two different hospitals in Guatemala and in each hospital there was a group of mothers who had contact right after birth for 45 minutes and a control group with the traditional separation after birth. After six months, the study in one hospital showed that the early contact group was breast feeding longer and showed greater weight gain than the control group, while the study in the other hospital showed no significant differences between the two groups. The second study involved fathers and showed that parental caregiving in the first three months of life was increased when the father was asked to undress his infant twice and established eye-to-eye contact for one hour in the first three days of life.

Why does this attachment develop? The authors suggest that maternal and infant behavior complement each other in many species-specific ways. There is a characteristic pattern of touching by the mother used in the first contact. Mothers have an interest in waking up infants to see their eyes open. Infants see at birth, and focus on the most interesting stimulus, the mother's eye. Some interactions originate with the mother, some with the infant. Infants respond to sound by some small movement like raising an eyebrow or moving a foot and this is a means of communication. Infants respond to odor as evidenced by the fact that breast feeding infants can distinguish between the breast pads of their mother and other mothers, at 5 days. Mimicry involving tongue protrusions, mouth open etc., occurs at two weeks.

There are other interactions that originate with the infant. In regard to eye-to-eye contact, mothers of blind infants have problems in feeling close to them. The arm's length distance for feeding and holding seems to be the focal distance best for the baby. The hungry cry of a healthy newborn increases the blood flow to the breasts. Breast feeding, licking and sucking stimulate the prolactin and oxytocin release which in turn increases milk production and letdown. Odor of the baby seems to the mother to be characteristic of the particular infant. The authors suggest that all these responses interact between mother and child, and they imply that these are species-specific and any disruption in them is unnatural and disastrous.

The theories of bonding and the crucial post-partum sensitive period these authors present are merely a form of the discredited, anti-social theory of biological determinism. It is true that obstetrical practices in this country are inhumane and serve to prevent full participation by the family. Involvement of the parents in the birth process and more early contact between parents and the infant would substantially improve the experience for all concerned.

There may well be certain phenomena observable in all human parent-child interaction. In the human species, however, such responses are of minor significance. We are intelligent social beings, whose fates are primarily determined by interaction with other people, what we learn from those interactions, and from other contact with the environment. Why then raise the issue of species-specific instinctual behavior, which is an evolutionary artifact, to such a level of importance? They do this because their theory serves the same purpose as other incorrect theories of the inheritance of intelligence or blaming the "matriarchal family" for lack of success of minorities. To give the "early sensitive period" the importance of determining the child's future is to mask the racism, sexism and rigid class divisions which truly determine the child's future. This is biological determinism; if you get the early nurturing that is appropriate for the species-specific pattern, you'll be fine, if you don't, you'll suffer forever. The result is to let the rulers of the society, who are also the ones who fund scientific research, off the hook. If the fault lies in those who fail—blaming the victim—society and thus those who rule society is blameless.

Jensen would blame bad genes, Moynihan blames the black family and the bonding advocates blame those who ignore the early sensitive period. The scientific error is the same—the absolutely false notion that correlation means cause and effect. The second error, perhaps too obvious, and made too many times to be other than by design is to use the race, sex and class biased IQ test as a measure of intelligence. These two "errors" in tandem produce a neat package: the poor have more broken families, they do less well on IQ tests and indeed they have less opportunity for early extended contact between mother and child. The conclusion is all too obvious: poor people and minorities are genetically less well endowed, have less family support and are not bonded—that's why they don't succeed in society. This nonsense has been disproven over and over again, most recently by a Carnegie Commission Report which indicates that social mobility is virtually nonexistent in the United States and that mobility has not increased at all in the last one hundred years!

Having indicated the possible motivation for the scientifically invalid questions studies and conclusions about parent-infant interaction, the shortcomings of proposed improvements of childbirth practices based on species-specific behavior are listed below.

1. Postpartum deprivation of mother-child contact is not the source of the ills of our society. Capitalism which teaches us selfishness, racism and sexism is at the root of the problem. A perfectly bonded child can grow up to be a fascist or a soldier killed in an imperialist war.

2. These studies place the burden of life on the early period. Mothers are made to feel guilty for anything that occurs in their child's development because their early bonding was not sufficient.

3. Bonding would support the idea of keeping women at home and, therefore, is propounded today because it is useful to the system that has a decrease in jobs and an increase in unemployment.

4. When this concept of close mother-child interaction is extended it would tend to support movements for decreased day care support and a decrease in hospital beds and personnel. With home births, less hospital beds and personnel are needed, and this could be used as an excuse to close hospitals.

5. What happens to mothers as a result of bonding has not been studied or considered. Must her life be subordinated and her career abandoned so that the child will have enough eye-to-eye contact with mom? What about working class and minority mothers who have to return to work immediately? Would their children be inferior because they did not have enough contact with mom?

6. Dr. A Brazelton suggests that maybe all this prolonged and intimate contact between mother and child might lead to overprotectiveness. Early socialization of a child with its peers is important and independence must be encouraged.[2]

7. The role of the father as a parent is only minimally discussed while the emphasis is on the special nature of the mother-child interaction. This could be extended to giving the mother the major responsibility for child care, another step backwards in the struggle against sexism.

8. The approach of these advocates of bonding is another

example of biological determinism. If mother and child do not have this early interaction, genetically determined behavior patterns are disrupted. If bonding is not practiced, there isn't much that can be done in the future. Therefore, the importance of education is minimized and cutbacks in education are justified.

Summary

Bonding as it is advocated by these authors tends to support racism and sexism and prevents people from uniting to fight the cutbacks that will result in less childcare, education and health care. The future of our children will not be determined by how much eye contact they have with their mothers right after birth, but by how much we do to improve the world our children will see when they begin to look beyond the infant-parent relationship.

REFERENCES

[1] Klaus, M. H. and Kennell, J. H., *Maternal-Infant Bonding,* St. Louis, C. V. Mosby,, 1972.

[2] Brazelton, T. B. in Klaus, M. H. and Kennell, J. H., p. 57.

WHO BECOMES
A MOTHER?
WHAT KIND OF CARE
DOES SHE GET?

A QUESTION OF CHOCOLATE CHIP COOKIES

Phyllis Witte

It is a question of chocolate chip cookies,
such as
when do you give them out to the children,
before lunch as a snack
or after lunch as a treat?
Should you give them out with milk?
Should you give the children
the milk first then the cookies,
or the cookies and then the milk?
Perhaps juice would be better.
How many cookies should each child be given?
How many cookies could each child eat
at a given time?
Can a child of four hold as many cookies
as a child of six?
Should a child be allowed seconds?
What is the content of the cookies?
How many chips are in each cookie?
Would a child feel slighted if he or she
were to receive more chips in a cookie
than another child?
Are the chips made of real chocolate?
Is the cookie itself made from
white bleached flour or whole wheat ground flour?
Would the quantity of sugar in each cookie
have an effect on the child's behaviorial traits?
Do we have enough chocolate chip cookies
in the first place?
Perhaps we should serve graham crackers instead.

ON THE SEMANTICS AND POLITICS OF THE BIOLOGICAL MODEL[1]

Georgine M. Vroman, Ph.D.

Ramapo College, New Jersey

We are each trying to bring our own background and experience to bear on the common theme: how our children are socialized into adult women and men in our society, and the role of "hereditarianism" in this process. I will speak to you as a medical anthropologist, i.e., someone who uses a medical background in the study and practice of anthropology, a discipline which can be described as the study of the ways different peoples live and the value systems which give meaning to their lives. I hope to be able to throw some light on the reasons why biology (as part of the natural and exact sciences) holds such a privileged and largely unchallenged position in our society as a basis for opinions and standards, and I shall briefly discuss some of the consequences and potential dangers of this situation. In addition, I shall give a few examples to illustrate the limitations of using the "biological model" to characterize conditions in our society which may be better described as the consequences of our socialization process. I am speaking here of phenomena such as "sexism", "racism", and "ageism", which are but specific instances of the much wider problem of discrimination. In these cases perceived biological differences become the basis of the prejudice by which some judge and treat others. Differences in socio-economic background, ethnic origin, and opinions can provide similar bases for discrimination. Although no segment of our population is free from prejudices regarding other groups of people, these attitudes become particularly important in their consequences when they are held by those who have the power to make and implement decisions.

Socialization in our society takes place predominantly

through the channels of mass education and the media, that is, radio, television, and the printed word. Our educational system introduces and maintains the points of view considered as the "correct" ones by those who are its decision makers and agents. Because of our compulsory education system, these points of view stand a better than even chance of turning into the generally prevailing ones in our society, which, in turn, becomes the condition necessary for preserving them. In other words, the educational system is one of the most effective means of changing, or maintaining, the *status quo*, and it is not surprising that wherever a power struggle in the world of ideas and values exists, the educational system will be one of its prime targets. This general situation, characteristic of all modern societies, is compounded for our society by the historical circumstance that the United States is a country of immigrants.

This has led to deliberately giving the educational system the task of incorporating these strangers into our common culture as soon as possible. Handlin[7, 8] describes the two contradictory processes by which these immigrants—who appear to look, speak, dress, eat, smell and think differently from the "established" population—were indoctrinated into the "American Dream" on the one hand, while those in powerful positions tried to impose and preserve a value system slanted in their own favor on the other hand. Diamond[4] is among the anthropologists who have analyzed our country's educational system and the degree to which it has taken over the socialization process which was in the past—and in less-developed countries still is—the task of the children's family group and of the people with whom they came in daily contact. This has led, he writes, to education being seen as "the general admission ticket to the merry-go-round of social mobility" and to an "Increasing attrition of the family as the basic mediator between the person and society". Leacock[12] has studied the effect of cultural stereotypes held by teachers on the performance of the pupils. She found that the crucial factor for learning was not the quality of teaching and the command of the material on the part of the teacher, but the expectation the teacher had of the children's performance. By comparing

New York City schools in respectively lower-income Black neighborhoods, middle-income Black neighborhoods, and lower-income White neighborhoods, she discovered significant differences in the demands made on the children, with disciplined behavior stressed over achievement in the Black schools. It should be noted that, while in the past it was the school system itself interpreting the needs of a particular school population, we are now witnessing a reversal of this situation. The neighborhood, through the local school board, attempts to impose its requirements on the administration and curriculum of the local schools. In cities like New York the increasing demand for "teacher accountability" has led to serious confrontations between neighborhood groups and the educational establishment. A further source of misunderstandings in the schools has been the situation, described by anthropological linguists such as Hymes,[9] Labov,[11] and Bernstein,[1] which results from the insufficiently realized fact that teachers and pupils may indeed speak "different languages", not only in their use of vocabulary and grammar, but also in the ways they depend respectively on verbal and nonverbal modes of communication. Several of these authors have pointed out that the burden of having to be able to understand both "languages" usually falls on the person in the minority group.

Aside from the "mainstream" socialization process going on in the schools, there is still that other one learned from and shared with family group and peers. That is, if you will, the "grass roots" socialization process. Often ignored or dismissed, this is particularly important among the ethnic and racial minorities, those groups which are not participating on an equal basis in the communication system of "mainstream" America. To speak of the need for "dialogue" only underscores the fact that verbal forms of communication are considered the only valid ones by those in power.

When the "mainstream" points of view are being disseminated by those who do not question them, we get a situation where the *status quo* is seen as the norm. When over and over again the media portray values and a way of life to segments of the population which cannot attain them, the conditions for

45

confrontations and challenges to this *status quo* are being created. When these confrontations are serious enough new priorities have to be formulated in a hurry, and often people are called upon who are not prepared to bring long-felt needs into words. "Spokesmen" (rarely "spokeswomen") are then sought who *do* command the verbal mode of communication, but who may not be fully representative of the challenging contingent. As often happens, the opinions of these vocal few are then taken to be those generally prevailing among the discontented, and this may in turn create a backlash. We see this process, for example, in recent challenges to the preferential treatment of minorities which had been intended to compensate for past injustices (e.g., the Bakke case). It manifests itself as well in the resistance to the ERA amendment and in the growing strength of the "Right to Life" movement which opposes a woman's right to abortion on request. Time and resources are wasted when we try to solve crises instead of the problems which lead to these crises.

It is a mistake to think that socialization only takes place in childhood: it is an ongoing process throughout our lives. I should now like to discuss the "scientific" bias which pervades the value system into which not just our children, but all of us, are being socialized. The United States may well be the most extreme case of an industrial society dependent on advanced technology and scientific knowledge (and science in this context means both the natural and exact sciences). The high value our society places on education is reenforced by the fact that our technology cannot be applied or understood without scientific training, although most of us can learn to use its products. This circumstance has created both a comparatively small elite, who hold the means and the power to perpetuate this situation, and a relatively large group of people who either passively and unquestionably accept these conditions or reject them out of hand. (See, for instance, in the last category, the health food "addicts", members of certain religious cults or communes, and certain activists). There is only a very small minority which does not let itself be put off by complicated technical detail and which tries to address itself both rationally and emotionally to the social and moral issues involved.

It is not at all impossible to come to an informed opinion in these matters, but it requires effort and it leaves no room for complacency. Some of us should not so confidently try to speak for others, and all of us should take the trouble to become informed and to share with others those thoughts that are important to us. Until this happens, however, we must remain aware of the circumstance that the importance of technological and scientific knowledge for our way of life has made these accomplishments the basis of the standards by which much of our intellectual endeavor is being measured. This condition has "spilled over" into the ways and the terms by which people's thoughts and actions are being judged; take for instance our distrust of "emotional and intuitive" ways of thinking. Few of those who lack this kind of technical and scientific knowledge feel competent to challenge arguments which are derived from "science", or which are couched in "scientific" language. And this, I think, creates the condition that "scientific" justifications for political decisions seem so convincing and so difficult to refute. Even among social scientists there seems to be a sense of inferiority evident in their relationship with natural and exact scientists. This is so, even though most social scientists have accepted Kuhn's position[10] that *all* sciences evolve in an essentially similar fashion.

It must not be concluded that there is no legitimate place for the "scientific method", the method of reaching conclusions on the basis of careful observation and logical thought which has been developed so effectively for the natural and exact sciences. Neither can we dismiss all biological approaches to our study of the human condition. Who can deny that women and men have different biological reproductive functions? But must these be seen as opposites or rather as complementary? And should we not ask ourselves how the *attributes* of masculinity and femininity have come into being, and for whose benefit they are being disseminated and perpetuated?

The "profit motive" is always a very telling one! Both history

47

and anthropology have made important contributions in this area by demonstrating how these gender attributes have changed throughout history, and are changing even in our own times, and how they are not the same for different societies or for different groups within our own society. In addition to "sexism" there are other areas where biology has been used as justification for discrimination, especially where this occurs on the basis of perceived ethnic and "racial" differences. One of the most interesting illustrations was the manipulation of public opinion in this country, regarding the supposedly inferior hereditary characteristics of immigrants from the Mediterranean and Asia area. This laid the groundwork for restrictive immigration legislation, in the 1920's coinciding, by the way, with a serious slump in the economy.[7] It was Franz Boas, one of the "fathers" of American anthropology, who demonstrated in a careful study that the small stature of these immigrants was not the result of inferior hereditary traits, but most likely of inferior nutrition, as their American-born children approximated the stature of members of the established population.[3] At the present time, when so many seem bent on reintroducing the principle of biogenetic determinism,[22] it may be fruitful to reread some of Boas's studies, documenting "race, language and culture as independent variables."[3]

Another important example of applying *perceived morphological* ("biological") markers is demonstrated by the use of the terms "race" and "color." These terms are often used to make distinctions in daily language as well as in technical publications on population and the epidemiology of diseases. In reality these are *social* distinctions because they result in value judgments and discriminatory practices. That this is so can be seen from the example of the Mississippi Chinese.[17] This group was imported in this area after the Civil War in the hope that they would replace the labor force lost after Emancipation. The Chinese were considered Blacks and intermarried with Blacks. Eventually, however, they left the work in the fields and settled down as small shopowners. At the same time they stopped intermarrying with Blacks and became increasingly regarded as Whites.

Some authors have suggested that we avoid using the terms "race" and "color" because of their association with "biological determinism" and propose the use of "ethnic" or "minority status" instead. I think this is a mistake. "Race" and "color" have a very specific meaning which would be lost if we were to use an "umbrella term" such as "minority status". As Vincent[24] has pointed out "ethnicity" implies not just an assigned but also a chosen identity. And a minority status can be based on almost any difference between groups, such as ethnicity, color, religion, language or sex.

Furthermore, I should point out that it is incorrect to equate "race" and "color", as some authors seem to be doing in discussing the situation in the United States, possibly because American Blacks have indeed been the most consistent and serious victims of racism. In this respect we must remember that the particular form of anti-Semitism which prevailed in Nazi Germany was also based on "race", but not on "color". In this case the discrimination was rationalized on the basis of presumed hereditary traits, considered to be common to all Jews, and branding them as of racially inferior stock.

"Color", in itself—and the darker the pigmentation the lower the social status[26]—is but one of the many "biological markers" which, together with socio-economic and behavioral characteristics, constitute that very complex phenomenon, a person's identity, whether presented or perceived.

In sum we can say that, in the case of racism, a person's total social and biological identity is reduced to his or her "race", that is to the presumed inherited biological identity. A further reduction takes place when, of all the many morphological characteristics of this person, the skin color is singled out as the most essential and reliable—because unalterable—one. That this manner of categorizing people is a form of biological determinism becomes evident, when we remember that American Blacks have occasionally been able to "manipulate" their racial identity, as perceived by others, by means of changes in dress, language use, or the company they keep.

As long as biological determinism, in whatever form it takes, remains a basis of distinguishing between people, and this, in turn, leads to discriminatory treatment, we must acknowledge its existence, and investigate why our society makes these distinctions, no less than what consequences result from this phenomenon.

There is a difference between "biology" as it refers to physiology and structure, and the so-called "biology" of biological bias which leads to social discrimination.

Biology can be defined as follows: It is in part a descriptive science of the way living organisms are built and it is also the study of the ways these organisms function. It should be made clear that both these aspects, structure and function, contain overt and latent elements of heredity, i.e., those characteristics passed on from the gene pool, and adaptations acquired during the organism's lifetime. By no means everyone using (or hearing) biological terms is aware of the existence of these two determining forces in biological processes, and of the fact that the so-called "nature versus nurture" debate is far from resolved. To translate this passage into human terms we could say: heredity determines whether one is born as, for instance, a Black female child, but society determines what it means to grow up as a Black woman. To give another example: it is known that Black men, in the United States, develop hypertension more frequently, at an earlier age, and in a more severe form than White men. Why this should be so has not yet been established with certainty. Lew[14] is of the opinion that this difference cannot be due to social stress, but is probably hereditary, because the same pattern was observed when Black middle-class men were matched with a control group of similarly employed and educated White men. Lew ignores the possibility that being Black may constitute a state of continuous mental and physical pressure, regardless of one's social position in life. Furthermore, it is not inconceivable that differences in the typical diet for Blacks, as compared to Whites, (specifically the intake of salt) may play a role in the different incidences of hypertension.[25] Instead of debating these points it might be more profitable to convince the most susceptible group, i.e., your Black men, to have regular checkups and to change their life style. But because hypertension in the early stages gives no subjective complaints, and especially because many in this prime target group have other more serious and immediate problems, such as poor housing and unemployment, this preventive measure in the early stage of this disease is far from effective. The concept of preventive medicine itself presupposes that one's present way of life is worth preserving and sacrificing for; but this may be a very unrealistic premise in the case of many among this particular segment of the population. In other words, it is never sufficient to look only at the symptoms of a patient; she or he must be considered as a sick person within a particular historical and socio-economic context. We thus see how misleading and incomplete a picture we get if we concentrate on the physical aspects of a major health problem of a particular minority group. Another form of "biological" or "bio-medical" bias is demonstrated in the use of terms derived from biology and medicine to characterize conditions that are of a social nature, such as: "normal", "functional", and especially "pathological". All of these are arbitrarily, even ethnocentrically, derived characterizations, more often than not applied to social conditions, and reflecting the particular point of view of their users. The long-established habit of using the "medical metaphor" is particularly suspect. Not only is the word "pathological" to describe social conditions a derogatory term; it shifts the blame and responsibility from those in a position to rectify these conditions to the victims.[2]

Specific examples of the harm caused by the use of the term "pathological" are the sociologically popular concepts of *"the culture of poverty"* and of *"the pathological matriarchal Black family"*. The first was introduced by Oscar Lewis[16] and has been extensively debated and disputed by authors such as Leacock[13] and Valentine.[23] The "pathological matriarchal Black family" was a characterization by Moynihan, and, because of his powerful position it has had important political ramifications. Billingsley[2] has given a concise, well-documented refutation of this way of characterizing the Black ghetto family. He found the poor Black family varied in structure, and generally capable of sharing and helping one another in difficult circumstances; this pattern was not limited to the immediate family but included neighbors as well. This last circumstance, added to the care and concern of both parents for their children (and most Black families were headed by men!) enabled many poor Black families to do a very good job of raising their children with limited economic resources. (See also Stack[20] on the extensive network of reciprocal rights, obligations, and exchanges between kin and pseudo-kin, that maximizes the available emotional and material resources among certain Black families on welfare.)

In my own work I have found that the "normal" that is, "mainstream"—American nuclear family (father, mother and their children) does not seem particularly flexible in dealing with adversity. For instance I found that Black male stroke patients almost always had a home to return to, if not that of their "own" family, then that of a sister or a cousin, or even a parent. On the other hand, several of their White male counterparts proved too heavy a burden for their wives to carry by themselves, and these men had to go to a nursing home. In contrast to the Black men, the family resources of these White male patients seemed much more limited and even inadequate, especially when the patients were old.

The medical care system in our country has, as in most Western industrialized countries, a strong biological basis *and* bias, i.e., diagnoses are primarily based on morphological and physiological observations. The anthropological literature shows that this is not the case in most other health care systems, especially in so-called folk medicine, where sorcery, revenge by spirits, and disturbances of the state of moral and physical balance; are recognized as agents of certain diseases.[6,18] Biological bias in our society puts a certain stigma on those suffering from mental disorders. As a matter of fact, specifically among minority groups, the patients fear of being branded as "crazy" may prevent both patient and doctor from respectively seeking and providing the right kind of help. It is known, for instance, that old people go from doctor to doctor to find relief from physical complaints (e.g., headache, insomnia). When a patient finds a sympathetic listener this turns out to be much more effective than tests and medication. The only problem is to find the person (and the environment) best suited for this "treatment".

Another important form of bias in our medical system is that it is male-oriented. If we look at medical textbooks we get the strong impression that the male patient is seen as the norm, and the female patient as a variation (if not an aberration) of this norm. Feminists have shown us the strong male bias in traditional psychoanalysis.[19] Treatment has usually been directed towards acceptance of the *status quo* which favors the male.

The general condition of women-as-patients is only in its very first stages of exploration. I mention the circumstance that there is still a strong sex-based hierarchy in the practice of medicine: i.e., the doctors are still predominantly male while the nurses and most of the other "helping" health professionals are still predominantly female. There is a similar division for members of the different "racial" and ethnic groups. Stein[21] has described some of the important consequences in attitudes and behavior of this division of labor and status coinciding with a difference in sex, and reflecting the traditional dominance of male over female in our society. When a woman patient enters into the strongly traditional male-dominated bastion of male-biased medical knowledge, her chance of being served according to her needs, and treated as a human being with equal rights as her male counterpart, are far from self-evident. Aside from those areas that have to do with her female reproductive and sexual functions (and even here it is often the male doctor or priest who will make the decisions for her), there are, possibly, different needs in women which are the result of their socialization as female-in-their-society. It then becomes possible that women-patients are seen as "different" (or even a "difficult") kind of patient. Analogous situations can be found when a patient belongs to a minority group, only minimally represented in the health professions. And even those comparatively few representatives of these groups entering these professions will have been trained to a large extent in the existing—and biased—value system of these professions! Old people in our society may also be subjected to bias in a value system which favors youth and vigor. Lewis and Butler[15] on the other hand, have described old age as the final stage of *growth* in the human life cycle. Obviously a great deal more can be said about how inequities and discrimination in our society are reflected in the ways people behave and are treated when they are ill. Not just differences in economic and other resources have an important determining influence, but also the differences in the ways all of us have been socialized.

What lessons can we learn from the material presented in this paper? What are the possible recommendations? In the first place, we must become aware of the biological bias in our society's value system, and of the ways in which it has become part of our ongoing socialization process. We must realize that because of this situation "biological" arguments for discrimination are very powerful indeed, and we must not shirk our responsibility to become informed as far as available knowledge permits. We must learn to be suspicious of this kind of justification, and to become aware of the role *we* can play in either continuing or breaking the vicious circle of misinformation leading to injustice which in its turn maintains the misinformation. As consumers (men and women, adults and children) of our medical care system, we must learn how to make the system work for us.[5] This means that our socialization process, in the schools, in the media, and with the help of "health advocates" must train us how to be patients and how to participate in our own health care. The medical professions must be trained to treat patients not as "cases", but as individuals with personal and socio-cultural histories of their own. Respect for one's self and for others seems to be the minimal requirement in this process.

NOTES

(1) This paper is in part based on material used in a dissertation presented for the degree of Doctor of Philosophy at the Graduate Facility of Political and Social Sciences of the New School for Social Research, in December, 1979.

(2) This use of the medical metaphor was the focus of a panel discussion on *Health Care and Social Policy* at the 1975 annual convention of the American Association for the Advancement of Science.

REFERENCES

1   Bernstein, Basil, A sociolinguistic approach to socialization. *In* Gumperz, John J., and Dell Hymes, eds., *Directions in Sociolinguistics*. New York, Holt, Rinehart and Winston, 1972.

2   Billingsley, Andrew, Family functioning in the low-income Black community. *In* Sussman, Marvin B., ed., *Sourcebook in Marriage and the Family*, 4th edition. Boston, Houghton Mifflin, 1974.

3   Boas, Franz, *The Mind of Primitive Man*. New York, The Free Press, 1963.

4   Diamond, Stanley., Epilogue. *In* Wax, M. L., Diamond, S., and Gearing, F., eds., *Anthropological Perspectives on Education*. New York, Basic Books, 1971.

5   Ehrenreich, Barbara and John, *The American Health Empire: Power, Profits, and Politics*. New York, Vintage Books, 1970.

6   Fabrega, Horatio and Mamming, Peter K., The experience of self and body. Health and illness in the Chiapas Highlands. *In* Psathasm George, ed., *Phenomenological Sociology*. New York, John Wiley and Sons, 1973.

7   Handlin, Oscar, *Race and Nationality in American Life*. Boston, Little, Brown, Co., 1957.

8   Handlin, Oscar, (ed.) *Immigration as a Factor in American History*. Englewood Cliffs, N.J., Prentice-Hall, 1959.

9   Hymes, Dell, Models of the interaction of language and social life. *In* Gumperz, John J., and Dell Hymes, eds., *Directions in Sociolinguistics*. New York, Holt, Rinehart and Winston, 1972.

10 Kuhn, Thomas S., *The Structure of Scientific Revolutions*. 2nd edition. Chicago, Univ. of Chicago Press, 1970.

11 Labov, William, *Sociolinguistic Patterns*. Philadelphia, Univ. of Pennsylvania Press, 1972.

12 Leacock, Eleanor Burke, Theoretical and methodological problems in the study of schools. *In* Wax, M. L., S. Diamond, and F. Gearing, eds., *Anthropological Perspectives on Education*. New York, Basic Books, p. 175–178, 1971.

13 Leacock, Eleanor Burke, (ed.) *The Culture of Poverty, a Critique*. New York, Simon and Schuster, 1971.

14 Lew, Andres A., High blood pressure, other risk factors and longevity: the insurance viewpoint. *In* Laragh, John H., M.D., *Hypertension Manual: Mechanisms, Methods, Management*. New York, Dun-Donnelly Publ. Co., 1973.

15 Lewis, Myrna I., and Butler, Robert, Life-review therapy. Putting memories to work in individual and group psychotherapy. In *Geriatrics*, vol. 29, no. 11, 1974.

16 Lewis, Oscar, The Culture of Poverty. In *Anthropological Essays*. New York, Random House, 1966.

17 Loewen, James W., *The Mississippi Chinese. Between Black and White*. Cambridge, Mass., Harvard Univ. Press, 1971.

18 Madsen, William, Value conflicts and folk psychotherapy in South Texas. *In* Kiev, Ari, M.D., ed., *Magic, Faith, and Healing*. New York, The Free Press, 1964.

19 Miller, Jean Baker, M.D., *Psychoanalysis and Women*. Baltimore, Md., Penguin Books, 1973.

20 Stack, Carol B., *All Our Kin. Strategies for Survival*. New York, Harper and Row, 1974.

21 Stein, Leonard, Male and female: the doctor-nurse game. *In* Spradley, James P. and David W. McCurdy, eds., *Conformity and Conflicts*. 2d. edition. Boston, Little, Brown and Co., 1971.

22 Tobach, Ethel, Gianutsos, John, Topoff, Howard, Gross, Charles, In *The Four Horsemen. Racism, Sexism, Militarism and Social Darwinism*. New York, Behavioral Publications, 1974.

23 Valentine, Charles A., *Culture and Poverty. Critique and Counter Proposals*. Chicago, Univ. of Chicago Press, 1968.

24 Vincent, Joan, The structuring of ethnicity. In *Human Organization*, Vol. 33, no. 4, pp. 375–379, 1974.

25 Mausner, Judith S., and Bahn, Anita, K., *Epidemiology*. Philadelphia, Pa., Saunders, 1974.

26 Daniels, Roger and Kitano Harry, *American Racism.* Englewood Cliffs, N. J. Prentice Hall, 1970.

VIEWS ON CHILDBEARING AND ECONOMIC IMPERATIVES

Helen Rodriguez-Trias, M.D.

Roosevelt Hospital

An attractive brochure was widely circulated among industrialists in Puerto Rico during the past decade.[1] It shows a diagram representing a pregnant woman whose protuberant abdomen contains, not a fetus, but a cogwheel. The title "Advantages of an In-Plant Family Planning Service" is followed by a dollars and cents account of the cost to the manufacturer of each pregnancy of a worker versus the cost of contraceptives. It ends with a boldly printed balance of $910 as savings for the industrialist per pregnancy prevented.

Although at first glance the promotion of family planning services in the workplace seems totally innocuous, if not downright beneficial, its portrait of women bears close scrutiny. It shows woman as a factory, a mere mechanical means of production of children and, therefore, as are all means of production, in the controlling hands of the factory owners. Childbearing thus becomes a production process to be controlled by them as their needs may dictate.

Puerto Rico all too often lays bare the trappings of the colonial relationship. As a direct colony of the United States, it is used in ways that less colonized countries seldom allow. Patterns of industrialization and their impact on women illustrate this well. Industrialization there was literally built on the backs of the Puerto Rican workers, nearly fifty percent of whom are women. The industries established in the early forties and fifties which formed the basis for U.S. corporate control of the Puerto Rican economy employed women garment, tobacco, textile and electronics workers. A hungry mass

58

of women was incorporated into the available workplaces. The Puerto Rican peasant and domestic worker quickly became the industrial worker. This massive transformation took place without any concurrent development of family support services. Coupled with the foregoing was the crescendo move to sterilize women initially by U.S. funded private foundations, and finally by the government of Puerto Rico. Not surprisingly, by 1968, Puerto Rican women had the highest sterilization rates in the world. Fully one-third of Puerto Rican women of childbearing age were by that time sterilized.[2] A legitimate question we raise, as a result is, "who controls fertility?" The answer may show that the right to choose is often an academic one.

Recently, *The New York Times* ran a front page story titled "Job Threats to Workers' Fertility Emerging As A Civil Rights Issue".[3] Several women attested to having sought sterilization operations in order to continue working in occupations which exposed them to chemicals or radiation judged to be harmful to eggs and unborn children. These workers for the Allied Chemical Company exposed what is actually a nationwide scandal: the pressure on women to cease their childbearing on demand of their employers. Again, women are viewed as baby factories to be set into production or not as the needs of the factory owners may require.

Women's employment, long the most labile of all employment, certainly shows the characteristics of marginal labor which responds to immediate economic imperatives. No longer is biology touted as determinant of women's occupation, but rather crass economic moves dictate the dominant theme. Women may be riveters, welders, or miners if it is wartime and male workers are scarce, but unfit for those rough occupations in recessions and times of increasing unemployment. Then they must retire to the "safety of home."

The Allied Chemical workers are exposing the situation which now prevails. Industrialists are not going to clean up the workplace or deal with the pollution that is affecting us all. They will rather fire workers or force them into sterility. The invocation of "hazards to the fetus" is but a cover-up of the push to remove women from highly paid skilled work and to undercut the demands for a clean workplace of unions such as the Oil, Chemical and Atomic workers. The gender role is used to scapegoat women and ultimately to keep all workers from advancing.

The avowed concern for the offspring of women in the skilled jobs is in sharp contrast to the deliberate exposure of men, women and children farm workers to pesticides on a daily basis. Agribusiness shows no qualms when it employs whole families for starvation wages in its polluted fields. Clearly, women's responsibility to the future is only considered when it can be used to push women out of well paying jobs. If they are of the highly exploited sector of workers, their biology can be waived.

Current policies on abortion and sterilization show a similar set of contradictions. On the one hand, a Hyde amendment prohibits the use of public funds for abortion services; on the other, sterilization operations are not only funded, they are positively encouraged, if not pushed, on women on welfare.[4] Since sterilization operations are costly procedures, it is difficult to justify the policy of preferential funding on a monetary basis. Even on metaphysical grounds, it is difficult to reconcile an abhorrence towards abortion with a pro-sterilization policy. In an existential sense, sterilization interferes more with human life since it eliminates the potential for its creation than does abortion, a temporal and finite act.

Promoted views on childbearing are thus seen to follow economic imperatives which may at some point dictate increase or decrease in population; or increase for some and decrease for others; or any combination of the above. Dishonesty is evident in the lip service presently given to the divine right to life and to a resuscitated romantic image of motherhood. At the same time, most women's choices are being reduced by the worsening economic situation as well as by ruthless cuts in childcare, educational, health and social services.

Sterilization itself raises many issues. Long reserved for the "unfit" since its introduction toward the end of the last century, it shows a dreadful continuum in its use today.[5] In the first half of the twentieth century many diseases as well as social evils were alleged to be hereditary and preventable only by ending the procreative powers of the bearers. None other than Justice Oliver Wendell Holmes gave weight and respectability to those prevalent views by his opinion on the constitutionality of the Virginia law which justified the compulsory sterilization of 18 year old Carrie Buck in 1924. He stated, "the principle that sustains compulsory vaccination is broad enough to cover cutting the fallopian tubes." He concluded that "three generations of imbeciles are enough."[6] Since the Indiana Legislature approved the first such law in 1909 similar laws were passed in thirty-three states and in the United States colonies including Puerto Rico. No less than 63,000 people were compelled to be sterilized for so-called eugenic reasons through 1964.[7]

The second half of the century has witnessed changes in tactics but not in the intent of the control of the people. The coercive sterilizations of low income women and of those belonging to Third World groups is now rationalized by the need to end the cycle of poverty. Dr. Curtis Wood, past president of the Association for Voluntary Sterilization, said: "People pollute, and too many people crowded too close together may cause many of our social and economic problems. As physicians, we have obligations to the society of which we are a part. The welfare mess, as it has been called, cries out for solutions; one of these is fertility control."[8] Perhaps in this last quarter of the century we are approaching another sinister version of the eugenics rationale. Now it will be the use of sterilization to prevent the birth of children handicapped by defects secondary to their own exposure, or the exposure of their parents' gonads to teratogenic chemical or physical agents. What an irony, if through these recently recognized and intensified human-made hazards, the dichotomy of acquired versus inherited comes to an end.

Through recorded history women have been told to bear children more often than now. Malthus formulated the concern that the English working class would overwhelmingly outnumber their affluent rulers. He originated the notions of birth restriction and selection by the powerful of who among the powerless is to survive. Today, these notions are couched

61

in chic terminology as "triage." When most eugenic laws were passed in the United States, in the second decade of this century, there was a growing concern among the well-born that the birth rates for the more affluent Anglo-Saxon stock were dropping while those of the immigrants from southern and eastern Europe, and, of course, blacks, were on the increase. President Theodore Roosevelt referred to this discrepant demographic index as evidence of "race suicide".[9]

There have been, however, more clearly stated goals than just the prevention of births of the "unfit", however these may be defined. Clearly aggressive family planning programs both in the United States and in the Third World have been aimed at producing stability that expanding multinational corporate interests so crave. The Alliance for Progress was created to develop U.S. corporate hegemony over Latin America in the most expeditious and least disruptive manner. The head of its Population Office, Edgar Berman, in 1966 presented a formula describing the relationships as Population Growth (PG) divided by Economic and Social Development (E + SD) as equal to Political Instability (PI).[10] The following quote from an interview in the *St. Louis Post Dispatch* in 1977 with Dr. Rt. Ravenholdt almost belabors the point.

> "First, he said, a decline in the growth rate in poor countries will increase those nations' standard of living. Resources divided by population equals well being. We're trying to lower the denominator in that equation. Second, the U.S. has a moral responsibility to take leadership because it was largely American medical advances that created the population explosion by lowering the world's death rate. We will be in a reprehensible position unless we help those poor countries balance their births and deaths. Third, population control is needed to maintain the normal operation of U.S. commercial interests around the world. Without our trying to help these countries with their economic social development, the world would rebel against the strong U.S. commercial presence. The self-interest is a

compelling element. Fourth, continuation of the population explosion, would result in such terrible socioeconomic conditions abroad that revolutions would result. These revolutions could be harmful to the U.S."[11]

The Agency for International Development that still has the Office of Population that until recently Dr. Ravenholdt headed, is heavily involved in population control. Since 1968, U.S.A.I.D. funds have accounted for more than half the total spent internationally. The monies spent for population control are now in a two-to-one ratio with those spent on health programs.[12] Their indecent interest in our fertility thus becomes more comprehensible when seen in the light of expanding U.S. corporate interests overseas and profits in the U.S.

Women are especially targeted as a vehicle for population control in a more subtle way by the Population Council, a group long involved in the purveying of a Neo-Malthusian theory and program.[13] Recognizing that women the world over have resisted those programs which they have seen as inimical to their view of themselves, their families and their future, the Population Council tries a new pitch—"development." The inclusion of women in "development" efforts is necessary in order to overcome their resistance. Unfortunately, "development" is not ever defined as meeting the needs of the people of the nation involved.

Once more Puerto Rico serves as an illustration of what "development" may mean when we consider persistent poverty despite mass migration, mass sterilization and a sad case of overdevelopment. It clearly shows that development is unhealthy without concern for the people, the environment or a solid economic basis of industry to provide needed goods for people. It behooves us as women, the subjects and objects of much of this social manipulation of gender stereotyping, to analyze the propaganda shifts and programmatic emphases and to determine what interests are behind them. We must produce our own set of priorities in the context of social changes favorable to us and to all the working people.

We must be clear on the exploitative nature of work in this

society and begin to ally with the trade unions on issues that bridge our understanding. We must recognize the long life that racism enjoys in this country where it has been used to justify oppression and even genocide. We must begin to bare its use so that we may keep it from dividing us. We must understand how pervasive the Neo-Malthusian ideology is and how it urges us to focus on population control so as to keep us from focusing on the ownership of wealth. We must not be fooled by the new slogans of development which co-opt our aspirations for equality and for a decent life and instead develop us as ideal workers and consumers. We must ask ourselves for whose benefit is this development.

REFERENCES

1 "Advances of an In Plant Family Planning Service", *Associacion Por Bienstar de La Familia*, Puerto Rico, 1964.
2 Vasquez-Calzada, J., "La Esterilizacion Femenina en Puerto Rico" *Nevista de Ciencias Sociales*, San Juan P.R. 17, No. 3, p. 281–308, 1973.
3 Shabecoff, Philip. The New York Times, p. 1, January 15, 1979.
4 Rodriguez-Trias, H., The Womens' Center Reid Lectureship, Barnard College, Women's Center, New York, p. 27, 1976.
5 Ehrenreich, Barbara and English, Diedre, in *For Her Own Good*, Anchor Press, Garden City, N.Y., p. 283, 1978.
6 Chase, Allen, in *The Legacy of Malthus*. Alfred A. Knopf, New York, p. 315, 1977.
7 Chase, Allen, in *The Legacy of Malthus*. p. 15–16.
8 H. Curtis Wood, "The Changing Trends in Voluntary Sterilization", *Contemporary Obstetrics and Gynecology*, 1 No. 4, p. 31–39, 1973.
9 Chase, Allen, in *The Legacy of Malthus*. p. 54.
10 Mass, Bonnie, Puerto Rico a Case Study of Population Control, *Latin American Perspectives*, 15 Vol. IV, No. 4, p. 73, 1977.
11 St. Louis Post Dispatch, April 22, 1977.
12 *Population Reports Family Planning Programs*, No. 51, March 1977.
13 Zeidenstein, George, *Including Women in Development Efforts*, The Population Council, New York, 1978.

STERILIZATION IN PUERTO RICO: COERCION OR PERSONAL CHOICE?

Iris O. López

Columbia University

Puerto Rico has the highest rate of sterilization in the world. By 1968, 35.5% of the female population in their reproductive years had been sterilized.[25] In attempting to explain the widespread use of sterilization among Puerto Rican women, many social scientists have posited cultural explanations such as female psychology, disruptive family organization, lack of adequate interspousal communication and the "grass roots demand" for this operation.[18,22,24] The "grass roots demand" for sterilization among Puerto Rican women has been taken to imply that these women are exercising reproductive freedom. Proponents of this "voluntary" view of sterilization tend to underemphasize the role which women's socio-economic conditions play in their fertility decisions. Moreover, they argue that the prevalent receptivity for sterilization among Puerto Rican women is based on the belief that Puerto Rican women consider sterilization as the safest and most effective form of "birth control."

In contrast to this argument, however, a smaller number of social scientists suggest that factors such as employment, socio-economic status and the health-care delivery system are equally or sometimes more influential in determining women's fertility choices.[8,19] The objective of this paper is to raise questions about the voluntary nature of sterilization among Puerto Rican women and to advance further lines of inquiry by examining why women whose primary roles traditionally defined as mothers and wives would choose a method of fertility control which requires them to relinquish forever their reproductive capacity rather than providing them with the ability to manage their fecundity. Furthermore, in order to acquire a more holistic view of this issue it is necessary to examine women's fertility decisions in conjunction with the evolution of sterilization on the island and within the historical and economic context of Puerto Rico's political status *vis-a-vis* the United States.

Many anthropological studies have demonstrated that the family and the division of labor within the household are primarily conditioned by the larger economy.[15,16,28] Historical and cross-cultural research also suggests that family and kinship structures, fertility rates and household composition change as household members find new sources of employment.[6,9,11,14,20,21,27] Women's participation in the labor force in Puerto Rico provides evidence for this. In 1899, only one year after Puerto Rico became a colony of the United States, women constituted 9.9% of the labor force. Women's participation in the labor force continued to increase as the agricultural structure of Puerto Rico's economy shifted from subsistence activities to the intensive commercial production of sugar and tobacco. The needlework industry likewise increased in importance during this period. The tobacco and needlework industries were of portentous significance for the status of women on the island for they incorporated a large number of women into the labor force.

Although women had participated in agricultural activities prior to this period, their roles were considered subordinate in importance relative to the role played by male workers.[17] In the needlework and tobacco processing plants, however, women were represented in greater numbers than men and had a greater responsibility in the elaboration and production of the end product. Moreover, with greater participation in the labor force there was, likewise, greater opportunity for women to participate in the labor struggles of the time. A major change in the Puerto Rican labor scene during the twentieth century was the emergence and development of a strong trade union movement.

The decade of the 1930s in the United States was also one of labor unrest culminating in the emergence of new groups and labor unions. In this panorama of increasing unemployment and depressed economic conditions, the United States authorities felt it necessary to curtail the large influx of immigrants to the United States. Eugenic and heredity theories became part of the ideology dominating population policy in the United States and were applied to immigration policy as well. The eugenic laws called for sterilization of specific sectors of the population who were considered to represent a threat to the society. As Mass has noted: "Programs aimed at eugenic objectives were implemented through anti-miscegenation laws in 24 US states in 1930 and through laws calling for sterilization of criminals, the feebleminded and the insane in 30 US states and 2 Canadian provinces."[13]

Just as economic distress in the United States led to the establishment of the eugenic laws in the thirties, similarly chronic unemployment, extremely low wages and deteriorating conditions in Puerto Rico prompted the transfer of these laws to the island. In 1937, Acts No. 116 and 136 were passed in Puerto Rico for individuals believed to fall within the category of "social undesirables" as well as for "health reasons".[8] Another provision of this law was the use of sterilization in cases of financial poverty and/or multiparity. In 1939, however, multiparity as a criterion for sterilization was eliminated but implementation of the law was still permitted for "health reasons." A director of the Family Planning Program in San Juan noted: "The original provision of the law was stretched from its 'health only' provision to the indigent population in general and finally quite simply to the woman who wished to terminate reproduction. The process of acceptance of sterilization was as follows: medical need . . . socio-economic need . . . anyone."[8]

In the implementation of population policy the practices of the health system as a whole are critical for an understanding of the widespread use of sterilization on the island. For example, during the thirties a survey of the attitudes of Puerto Rican physicians towards sterilization was taken. Eighty percent of those doctors responding favored sterilization as a medical solution to malnourishment and poor health. Since malnourishment and poor health were so widespread among the lower-income strata, sterilization was in effect condoned for the Puerto Rican population at large. The attitudes of physicians are also important in understanding the widespread use of sterilization on the island. Another prevalent attitude among physicians during this time was that contraceptive methods were too difficult for lower-income Puerto Rican women to follow. Moreover, doctors were of the opinion that lower-income individuals could not be trusted with birth control, since "contraceptive devices are not practical for the majority of people, only for the more intelligent."[1] Postpartum sterilization, therefore, would eliminate the need for continued individual cooperation in fertility control by putting an end to reproduction once and for all. Sterilization indeed was the most effective solution to the "population problem." In the words of a medical director of a group insurance program:

> ". . . they were pushing (sterilization) in health centers—there was a program of sterilization in Puerto Rico. This was in the fifties, they were sterilizing a lot of women then. They were not being forcibly sterilized. Rather it was a method that was feasible, because the pill did not exist then. It was not a government program *per se*. They simply gave women orientation and facilitated the operation for them. There were many government institutions that did it, they were doing it in great quantity, they did hundreds yearly."[8]

Although a concerted effort was made to curb population growth, deplorable economic conditions continued to prevail in Puerto Rico. Rather than reexamine the origin of the economic problems on the island and focusing on an economic solution that would be advantageous to Puerto Rico, a more dependent relation with the United States was encouraged. Operation Bootstrap, a program of economic development launched in the late forties by the United States and Puerto Rican governments purported to stimulate the island's economy by attracting foreign industry to Puerto Rico. One way in which this was accomplished was by offering manufacturers lucrative economic incentives such as tax exemption for a period of ten to thirty years. This program was clearly advantageous to United States corporations but the Puerto Rican population was in general negatively affected. With the intensification of industrialization, the agricultural sector became severely limited as a source of employment. This stimulated internal migration from rural to urban areas. Although Operation Bootstrap precipitated a brief boom, few jobs were created for the island inhabitants. The failure of this program to create sufficient jobs for its population was once again blamed on the imbalance between people and resources ("over-population"). In the fifties, massive migration took place to the United States. The successive shifts from labor intensive to the present capital intensive phase of industry with its need for a smaller labor force have increased unemployment and maintained low wages. As Marrero noted:

> "The average income of Puerto Ricans on the island has been estimated to be half of what is earned by the inhabitants of the state of Mississippi, the poorest state in the United States. Furthermore, the average wage of a Puerto Rican worker is equivalent to one third of what an American worker earns for doing the same kind of work. A comparison of average hourly earnings between Puerto Rico and the United States in the petroleum refining industry, prepared jointly by the Bureau of Labor Statistics from Puerto Rico and the United States Department of Labor in 1975, shows that Puerto Rican workers earned $3.19 per hour, while United States workers earned $6.35 for the same type of work. It is worth noting that the salaries paid by the petroleum refining industry are among the highest on the island. The labor cost differentials are even higher in other types of industries."[12]

Considering these conditions migration and sterilization should not be viewed as separate programs but as two phases of the same objective—population control. Despite the fact that emigration to the United States absorbed 83% of the natural population increase of Puerto Rico, sterilization was intensified.[13] So effective was the campaign which was mounted against population growth that by 1955, Puerto Rico had achieved the lowest population growth in the Caribbean. From 34.8 per thousand in 1956, Puerto Rico's birth rate fell to 28.3 per thousand in 1966. By 1965, approximately 35% of women of child bearing age had been sterilized; two thirds were still in their twenties. Competition for jobs may have provided an inducement for women to undergo sterilization. However, in the period extending approximately between 1946-1966, experiments with the pill and the I.U.D. were conducted on the island and Puerto Rican women were used as experimental subjects in the testing of these methods of contraception. The negative results of this experimentation left widespread distrust and fear of these methods of birth control, providing further inducement for the use of sterilization. As a result the birth control clinics which had mushroomed all over the island to serve the Puerto Rican population went unused.

Continued high unemployment perceived as a problem of "over-population" led much of the research during the fifties at evaluating and recommending ways of controlling the population problem on the island.[5,7,24] One of the most extensive studies undertaken during the fifties was Stycos, Hill and Back's investigation: *The Family and Population Control: A Puerto Rican Experiment in Social Change.* This study was particularly concerned with the underutilization of birth control facilities among the Puerto Rican population. After extensive research, they concluded that Puerto Rican couples were ambivalent about their reproductive goals, did not have the family organization necessary to establish these goals, and lacked adequate interspousal communication on family planning. They also inferred that Puerto Rican women opted for sterilization as the most effective method of "birth control."

A number of issues which interfered with the delivery of care in the birth control clinics were uncovered by the investigators. Among these were: clinic hours rarely corresponded with women's free hours; in many cases women had no one to care for their children; clinics were frequently out of supplies and there was a lack of adequate transportation to and from the clinics. In spite of this evidence, the investigators chose to emphasize attitudes and values favoring sterilization rather than the lack of alternative means of birth control. Thus women's fertility decisions were relegated to purely cultural considerations. Furthermore, this approach permitted the authors to gloss over the role that class and the social distribution of resources played in the quality of health care services which these women received. From the foregoing it is clear that cultural explanations which preclude the economic and social conditions in which women make their decisions do little to enhance our comprehension of why sterilization is so widely accepted among Puerto Rican women.

In order to understand the nature of Puerto Rican women's decisions for sterilization we must ask ourselves what factors predispose Puerto Rican women towards this operation. Are the conditions under which women make these decisions such that one could argue they constitute coercion and if so what type of coercion is involved? To do this women's decisions to be sterilized must be viewed in relation to the objective conditions of their lives. In the case of Puerto Rico, the high rate of unemployment and increasing economic insecurity are precipitating factors. In a recent study on the attitudes of the medical professions towards population and female sterilization, Henderson[8] demonstrated that doctors' attitudes and women's socio-economic status played an important role in women's fertility decisions (1976). For example, Henderson noted a higher rate of sterilization among working as compared to non-working women and found that lower-income women frequently cited the cost of living, a lack of perceived alternatives and the need to work as a major reason for getting sterilized. She also observed a correlation between high rates of sterilization and low-educational attainment. An island-wide survey undertaken in 1968, demonstrated that the highest rates of sterilization were found among women with the lowest educational achievement.[25]

In order to identify the factors which influence women's fertility decisions, it is also imperative to investigate the relationship between Puerto Rican women's views, ideology, knowledge of contraceptives, access to quality medical care, interpretation and use of sterilization, as well as how their choices are influenced or limited by their particular socio-economic position. However, it is not enough to recognize that the choice of sterilization involves cultural as well as structural components. We must also discover the specific context of behavior and, what is equally important, how people work out their problems and reach decisions within the institutional arrangements in their society.

The fact that so many Puerto Rican women find sterilization so readily acceptable may in part be explained by the limited alternatives provided by the health care system, such as the lack of safe and effective forms of birth control and reliable information regarding contraception, sterilization and abortion. Presently funds from medicaid, family planning programs and the Department of Health, Education and Welfare are readily available for sterilization in Puerto Rico. No such ready funding is available for abortion except in "narrowly" defined therapeutic cases.[4] This differential pattern of funding suggests a definite predilection on the part of the federal bureaucracy for sterilization over other available means of birth control. Furthermore, since 1960, the Department of Health, Education and Welfare has been funding 90% of all hospital costs incurred for sterilization, and this constitutes a strong inducement for promoting this procedure.[4] The ready funding of sterilization has also resulted in the emergence of clinics catering to or subsisting from revenues obtained from this operation.

Another factor which serves to encourage sterilization is the lack of adequate knowledge about sterilization or available alternatives which would help women in their effort to make informed decisions regarding their fertility choices. As CESA has noted: ". . . government funds in Puerto Rico have not been adequately used to set up clinics for counseling women in the use of less final methods of birth control.[4] It has been established that Puerto Rican women associate cutting of the fallopian tubes with permanent sterilization, whereas the tieing of the fallopian tubes is deemed to be a temporary method of fertility control. This has been documented by the

Center for Social Research, in a study they are presently conducting in New York City. According to some of their preliminary findings, eighteen out of twenty-six women who had been sterilized, believed that women who had their fallopian tubes "tied" rather than "cut" could become pregnant again. Thirteen out of the eighteen believed that they might become pregnant again.[4] In other words, the irreversibility of these procedures regardless of the method used, had not been made clear to them.

Although I have emphasized the structural components in this paper, this does not imply any underestimation of the cultural dimension. Rather I am suggesting that it is important to interrelate what aspects in the Puerto Rican "culture complex" permit the adoption of sterilization among Puerto Rican women, or how structure influences the cultural acceptance of this practice. Further, one must know how both aspects become integrated into a cohesive and meaningful whole which provides a guide for individual behavior. The widescale acceptance of sterilization has much to do with the ready availability of sterilization, the massive governmental support for this operation, the lack of adequate health-care services, the role of the health-care system and doctors' attitudes towards population policy and its relation to the lower classes. All this in the context of depressed economic conditions in Puerto Rico has guided women to "opt" for sterilization.

To assert that sterilization constitutes a "grass roots" acceptability is to let statistics take the place of analysis. It is quite true that the widespread use of sterilization necessitates some degree of individual acceptance. However, what is crucial to the understanding of the widespread acceptability of this practice is why and how it has gained such popularity as the "contraceptive method of choice." At some point the relationship between sterilization and population policy, and between sterilization and socio-economic status must be taken into account. Initially, women's socio-economic position; their so-called "laziness," men's fear of vasectomy, and women's presumed ignorance and unreliability in following contraceptive methods were all used as justifications for sterilization.

What we must ask ourselves is at what point did this justification for sterilization turn into "exercise of freedom of choice?"

REFERENCES

1   *Boletin de la Asociacion Medica de Puerto Rico*, Tubal Ligations: A Study of 351 Cases, 40:104–108, 1948.

2   Carasa, *Women Under Attack: Abortion, Sterilization Abuse, And Reproductive Freedom,* New York: Committee For Abortion Rights and Against Sterilization Abuse, 1979.

3   Centro de Estudios Puertorriquenos *(History Task Force) Labor Migration Under Capitalism*, New York: Monthly Review Press, 1979.

4   CESA, *Workshop on Sterilization Abuse*, New York: Sarah Lawerence College, 1978.

5   Cofresi, E., *Realidad Poblacional de Puerto Rico*, San Juan, Puerto Rico, 1951.

6   Engels, F., *The Origin Of The Family, Private Property And The State*. Edited by Eleanor Burke Leacock. New York: International Publishers, 1972.

7   Hatt, K. P., *Backgrounds of Human Fertility in Puerto Rico*. Princeton University Press, 1952.

8   Henderson, P. M., *Population Policy, Social Structure and The Health System In Puerto Rico: The Case Of Female Sterilization*. Unpublished Dissertation, University of Connecticut: Department of Anthropology, 1976.

9   Levine, D., *Family Formation In An Age Of Nascent Capitalism*. New York: Academic Press, 1977.

10 Lopez, I., *A Study Of Women and Social Change In Puerto Rico*. Unpublished paper, Columbia University: Department of Anthropology, 1976.

11 Mamdani, M., The Myth Of Population Control. New York: *Monthly Review*, 1972.

12 Marrero, Sonia, *Puerto Rico: The Kept Woman Of The United States?* Unpublished Thesis, Columbia University Graduate School of Journalism, 1977.

13 Mass, B., Emigration and Sterilization In Puerto Rico In *Population*

Target: The Political Economy Of Population In Latin America. Brampton, Ontario, 1976.

14 Medick, H., The Proto-Industrial Family Economy: The Structural Function Of Household And Family During The Transition From Peasant Society To Industrial Capitalism. *Social History*, 3, 1976.

15 Minge-Kalman, W., On The Theory And Measurement Of Domestic Labor Intensity. *American Ethnologist*, 4, 1977.

16 Minge-Kalman, W., Family Production And Reproduction In *Industrial Society: A Field Study Of Changes During The Peasant To Worker Transition In Europe*. Unpublished Ph.D Dissertation. Columbia University: Department of Anthropology, 1977.

17 Pico, Vidal, I., The History of Women's Struggle For Equality In Puerto Rico. In *Sex and Class In Latin America*. Edited by Helen Safa and June Nash, New York: Praeger Publishers, 1976.

18 Presser, H., *Sterilization And Fertility Decline In Puerto Rico*. Berkeley: University of California, Population Monograph No. 13, 1973.

19 Rodriguez-Trias, H., A Woman Doctor's Perspective On Women And The Health-Care System. In *The Womens' Center Reid Lectureship*, 1978.

20 Safa, H., Class Consciousness Among Working-Class Women in Latin America: Puerto Rico. In *Sex and Class in Latin America*. Edited by Helen Safa and June Nash. New York: Praeger, 1976.

21 Scott, J. W., Sources Of Social Change In Community, Family And Fertility In A Puerto Rican Town. *American Journal Of Sociology*, 72: 520–530, 1966.

22 Scrimshaw, S., *The Demand For Female Sterilization In Spanish Harlem: Experiences Of Puerto Ricans In New York City*. Presented at American Anthropological Meetings, 1970.

23 Silvestrini-Pacheco, B., Women As Workers: The Experience Of The Puerto Rican Woman In The 1930s. In *Women Cross Culturally: Change And Challenge*. Edited by Ruby Rohrlich-Leavitt. The Hague: Mouton, 1975.

24 Stycos, M., Hill, R., and Back, K. W., *The Family And Population Control: A Puerto Rican Experiment In Social Change*. University of North Carolina Press, 1959.

25 Vásquez Calzada, J., El Desbalance Entre Recursos Y Población En Puerto Rico. University of Puerto Rico, Center For Demographic Studies (mimeo), 1968.

26 La Esterilización Femenina En Puerto Rico, Universidad de Puerto Rico, Departamento De Epidemiología, Bioestadística, Ciencias Sociales y Demografía (mimeo), 1973.

27 White, B., Demand For Labor And Population Growth In Colonial Java. *Human Ecology*, 1, 1973.

77

28 White, B., The Economic Importance Of Children In A Javenese Village. In *Population And Social Organization*. Edited by Moni Nag. The Hague: Mouton, 1975.
29 World Health Organization, Technical Report Series, No. 512, 1973.

RACISM AND SEXISM
IN NURSING EDUCATION AND PRACTICE

Mary June Bayuk Gelles, R.N., B.S.N.E.

Teachers College, Columbia University

In examining the ways in which scientific knowledge is misused to foster racism and sexism, it is of interest to look at nurses and nursing education. As a participant of this conference I am considered a "layperson contributor." Now, that suits me fine, however, many from the "profession" for which I "trained" would consider that to be an insult. The point I am making is that since I "trained" to be a nurse, the occupation of nursing has been striving to be considered a profession.[1,2] I do think that the changes in nursing have been admirable for the profession, but professionalism and elitism can be a destructive element right along with racism and sexism. Racism, sexism, professionalism, are used to keep people divided. They prevent us from getting together to improve our lives, working conditions, and particularly medical care.

When I began nursing school in 1960, nursing was still considered an occupation for girls mainly from the lower income bracket. Tuition for three years of training cost $220, and we received $8.00 per month stipend (stocking money) and a scholarship of $50 per year. For somebody like me who really wanted to help people, it was affordable. Later I learned that nursing students were used to staff the hospital, and when this practice was discontinued the cost of tuition increased![3]

My class was composed of 115 students, mostly of Jewish background (but then it was Mount Sinai Hospital). We did have a few Italians, Irish, etc. but only 3 black students. No males or married students were allowed. One student was expelled when they found out she was married, and she was the only Puerto Rican in our class.

Sexism was an inherent part of the curriculum. Right from the beginning we were taught how to speak to "the doctors" in a manner which was a direct reflection of attitudes of women toward men. At one hospital to which we were affiliated we had to stand up if a doctor entered the room. Not only were there very few women doctors then, but those that were there were very bright (but not overly aggressive) and obviously denying their sexual identity. They were attempting to be barely noticeable as women.

In 1968 there was an article in the American Journal of Nursing which very accurately described the "Doctor-Nurse Game".

> *Object of the Game:* The object of the game is as follows. The nurse is to be bold, have initiative, and be responsible for making significant recommendations, while at the same time she must appear passive. This must be done in such a manner so as to make her recommendations appear to be initiated by the physician . . .

The nurse who plays the game well is considered a good nurse. The outspoken nurse is labeled a "bitch" or suffering from "penis envy" or just acting out hostility towards men.[4] So we were taught that if the doctor ordered a medication for a patient which was not the usual dosage, you said something like, "Gee, Dr. Jones, I've never seen that dosage given to anyone before, is that a new mode of therapy?" But, if the doctor did order a medication in the wrong dose, the issue of refusing to follow the doctor's order was serious and passed on to the supervisor. You can guess who would be blamed if the wrong medication or dose was given.

But if you think that because I speak of events 18 years ago, things have drastically changed I will have to dispel that illusion. In thinking about what I would say here today, I spoke to a friend who is a third year medical student and a nurse. She told me this story. In the last class of a course on Physical Diagnosis the Chairman of Medicine traditionally comes in to speak. In giving his closing statement his emphatic point was that in making a diagnosis a doctor must consider the "whole" patient. Remember, he said, being able to use your head and think is what differentiates doctors from nurses.

Along with the traditional sexual stereotypes, we were also taught racial stereotypes. We were told that Puerto Ricans were quite hysterical especially when ill and had to be treated differently. We were told that asthma, which we frequently saw among Puerto Ricans, was really a psychological condition. It was only later that theories of allergies was considered a more frequent cause. We were also told that Asians and Swedish people (nordic types) were stoic etc. etc. But once again this is not ancient history nor limited to the education of nurses. In the 1974 edition of Schwartz's *Principles of Surgery*, they make similar statements.[5]

Racism was also a very strong element when we were instructed how to deal with our auxiliary staff. Actually there was a similarity between how we were taught to deal with doctors and nurses aides. We were taught to be careful, gentle, and not overly aggressive. With doctors it was so that we wouldn't hurt their feelings, or insult them, but in the case of our minority staff, it was because of fear of them. Racist fear was taught to us by teaching racial stereotypes about how "those people" behaved. And I thought that Delia my Puerto Rican classmate was aloof because she was a snob? But the facts are that my class, like so many segregated classes had only four minority students. The only other minorities we met were the lowest paid hospital workers in housekeeping, in auxiliary jobs like nurses aides, unit clerks, transporters, and maybe a few in skilled jobs like engineers. There were one or two minority doctors, a few or no Registered Nurses, and a few Licensed Practical Nurses. None of our instructors were minorities. Studies have shown that minority students are more successful (fewer drop-outs) where there are more role models in the faculty.[6] Having more integrated classes and more minority students is essential to prevent the spread of prejudicial theories. Personal experiences with minority students can counteract false theories or result in a fight against their being taught at all. Minority admissions are necessary to achieve integrated nursing and medical schools to counteract racist and sexist theories.[7]

My ideas began to change by personal experience. At the beginning of my second year in nursing school I was assigned to a Neurological and Neurosurgical floor. I was to be the charge nurse. That was the usual practice in those days. There is no doubt that I would not have been able to survive, nor would many patients, had it not been for the skill of a nurses' aide who guided me through those three weeks. Yet we are taught terrible things about nurses aides. One only has to look at an article called "Getting Along Better with Those Aides."[8] The aides are pictured as sullen, lazy, antagonistic and irresponsible. Sound familiar? In the article "those aides" are, as to be expected, mainly black. A defense of nurses aides published the following year is good, but never mentions the racism inherent in the original article.[9]

After graduating nursing school I worked as a staff nurse, assistant head nurse, and then began teaching in Inservice Education. I was mainly responsible for teaching auxiliary staff. That is where I learned that most everyone who comes to work in a hospital does so to help people. Only their education limits the kinds of jobs they can do. They all wanted to learn and were extremely responsive to anything I taught that would help them to help the patients. But more often than not they were not rewarded for being resourceful. All they were expected to do was follow orders. Their enthusiasm was often squelched by the staff with whom they worked; often because of racism. I began to learn that simply trying to be fair is not enough. One had to oppose racism actively just as one had to oppose sexism actively.

The hospital workers were in a union and about that time a group of Licensed Practical Nurses began an organizing campaign. A group of Registered Nurses joined in the campaign. It became obvious to us that multiracial unity was a key element, and if this was achieved then unionism would be a real possibility. Our group felt that all nurses should be in the same union since we were all concerned with improving patient care and improving our economic situation. As you can guess we met with opposition because of professionalism.

"Nurses should have their own union," was the slogan of a group organizing for nurses to join another union for RN's only. They were supported by the hospital administration, and led by the nursing supervisors. Our combined group continued to meet, hold open meetings and collect signatures. We even held an open debate with the RN only union organizers. What suddenly happened was that the union organizing the LPN's convinced us that since they had a majority of LPN's signed up it would be best to get them in and work on the RN's separately. We mistakenly agreed perhaps because we were not sufficiently convinced of the need to overcome the racism and elitism among RN's. We were never able to win the RN's.

Now, I am a nurse in a city funded daycare center and a mother of three children. I applaud the idea of an International Year of the Child. But, I do not see this a reality in the world, or in New York City where children are not given any priority. I am assigned to work 15 hours a month in a day care center that has 180 children. That is what the city allows. A doctor visits 5 hours a month, whenever they can assign one to the center. I am a "nurse consultant" where a full time nurse would have too much work. Preventive medicine would not only save lives but would help these children to lead better lives. If we could diagnose physical problems, learning, hearing and speech problems before these children entered elementary school, their ability to learn would be enhanced. But, I barely have time to see that each child has a complete physical examination once a year. We only have office hours during the day and many working parents can't get off from work. They have to go to local Medical offices or Child Health Stations. The Child Health Stations usually do good examinations but I can't say the same for some of the private offices. Many parents work long hours in factories and taking time off is impossible because they may lose their jobs. Many are undocumented workers afraid of deportation and often working in factories where they are not allowed to receive calls even in medical emergencies. Often these parents don't speak English and although some of our doctors are bilingual, it's hard to get the parents in when a physician is there.[10]

The day care system saw a lot of action in the early 70's here in New York. Parents, mainly minority women, fought hard to win more and better day care centers and now these gains are being whittled away with cutbacks. Medical care or even supervision is difficult. The children who should have the TOP PRIORITY, absolutely don't. When Mayor Koch talks about cutbacks, *then* children are given high priority: their education and health care are cut first.

So, you see it comes full circle. The ideas that genes and gender explain differences leads to sexism and racism. All of us, women, men, black, white, professionals, medical workers, undocumented workers must see that it is in our interest to unite and oppose these ideas in order to achieve a truly healthy international world for our children.

REFERENCES

1 Cleland, Virginia, "Sex Discrimination: Nursing's Most Pervasive Problem," *The American Journal of Nursing*, Vol. 71, Number 8, pp. 1542–1547, 1971.
2 Levinson, Richard, "How Sexism in Medicine Has Kept Women Down and Out." *The American Journal of Nursing*, Vol. 76, Number 3, pp. 426–431, 1976.
3 *The Public Health of Racism in the United States*, The International Committee Against Racism, New York, 1978.
4 Stein, Leonard L., "The Doctor-Nurse Game," *The American Journal of Nursing*, Vol. 68, Number 1, pp. 101–105, 1968.
5 Schwartz, Seymour, Lillehei, Richard, C., Shires, G. Thomas, Spencer, Frank C., Storer, Edward H., in *Principles of Surgery*, New York, McGraw-Hill Book Co., p. 971, 1974.
6 Burgess, Audret L., "Baccalaureate Nursing Education and Minority Nurses," *Urban Health*, pp. 35–44, July/August, 1978.
7 *The Bakke Case: The Myth of Reverse Racism Revisited*, International Committee Against Racism, New York, 1977.
8 Wiley, Loy, "Getting Along Better With Those Aides," *Nursing 75* Vol. 5, Number 6, pp. 67–74, 1975.
9 Adams, Elaine, "From The Bottom Up: An Aide's View," *Nursing 76* Vol. 6, Number 4, pp. 98–101, 1976.
10 *Apartheid in the Clinic: Racial Segregation in U.S. Medical Care*, International Committee Against Racism, New York, 1978.

CHILDREN LEARN ABOUT THE WORLD

I AIN'T NO WEED!

by Lindamichellebaron

I think *some* kids come here
knowing everything
already.

Don't need no help.

Not me!!

I need nurturing.

Some kind, caring hands
helping me.

Some kids,
I say they weeds
don't need nothing.

Can know and do everything,
without no help.

Popping up with right answers,
without no nurturing.

Not me!!

I need time and care,
'cause a flower don't just
pop-up.

I need time and care,
'cause a flower has to be . . .

    petted by the sun . . .
    fed by the earth . . .
    refreshed by the rain . . .
    and protected by the maker . . .
Like me!!

'cause I ain't no weed,
like *some* kids is!!

JUST STARTING

Phyllis Witte

There is something about writing their letters from top to bottom, around and down, making sure they touch the line, the correct grip on the pencil,

There is something about line up, take off your shoes, put on your sneakers, do you have a hat, where are your gloves, did you sign the attendance sheet otherwise how do we know you're here?

There is something about time for music, time for art, time for gym, Nicholas you forgot it's time for reading, O.K. folks it's time to eat,

That rings of the goosestep, the click of the heel.

There is something about a child reading at age four, doing math at age five,

There is something about parents wanting their four year old to stay in school from 8:30 to 3:00, not understanding why he or she should come home early Friday afternoon,

and Jennifer being sleepy, and Peter unable to do a third page of math, or Pat not being able to write about his feelings because he doesn't know what his feelings are.

Troy can't draw a circle, but he can repeat answers.

90

There is something about the parents wanting their first-grader to learn French, and Anna cannot tell you that an apple is a fruit,

wanting them to take swimming lessons, dancing and ice skating lessons after school, wanting them to become champions.

And the teachers are concerned with their reading each and every day,

And the administration is concerned with the numbers that they can recruit each and every year,

And the parents, the parents want what is best, and to be happy for the rest of their own lives.

In short, they will be remarkable people when they grow up,

They will ring of the goosestep, the click of the heel.

JUST PUSH

by Lindamichellebaron

One day the teacher
Walked up to the room.
The door was closed,
and the keys inside.

The teacher tried the door,
but it didn't open.
We waited til he got
        another key.
That's when he realized
it was opened all along.
All he had to do was push.

Sometimes I think
he does us the same way,
has us waiting,
while he looks for the key
of knowledge,
to let us in.
When, really, all he has to do
is give us a little push
by just thinking
we can.

THE NUTRITION-INTELLIGENCE HYPOTHESIS: ANOTHER VICTIM-BLAMING THEORY

Arthur Schatzkin, M.D., M.P.H.

Mt. Sinai Medical Center
Columbia University School of Public Health

I have been asked to speak on the topic of nutrition and intelligence, particularly on the relationship of prenatal or infant malnutrition and subsequent intellectual ability.

The hypothesis has been advanced that subsequent intellectual capacity can be impaired as a result of events occuring in the early maternal-child relationship, namely, the malnourishment of the developing fetus or infant. The significance of such a proposition is mind-boggling. If, as some researchers have suggested, some 60% of the total pre-school population of the *world* (some 500 million children) suffer from "mild to moderate forms of protein-calorie malnutrition",[1] then we are faced with a phenomenon of staggering social and political implications.

The importance of this question for this conference is clear. If we accept the nutrition-intelligence hypothesis, we will have focused responsibility for mental deficiency squarely on the early maternal-child relationship. Whether we blame the mother for not feeding her unborn child or infant, or instead find the social environment "at fault" for the inadequate nutritional support, the fact remains that faulty child-rearing would be "causing" intellectual deficits in hundreds of millions of people throughout the world. To put it more bluntly: whether she provides inadequate nutritional support because of her own inadequacies or because she is the victim of social circumstances, the poor mother would be breeding dumb children. That's what this hypothesis really comes down to.

Victim-Blaming Theories

The relevance of the nutrition-intelligence controversy for this conference, however, goes beyond the "mere" grounding of reduced intellect in the early maternal-child relationship. We are dealing here with still another attempt to find scientific "explanation" for observed racial and socioeconomic differences, not only in "intelligence," but in all aspects of social life. This conference has been attempting to expose the intellectual fallacies and dangerous political implications of various hereditarian or sociobiological theories of sex, race, and class differences. These theories have been rightly attacked for attempting to perpetuate in the public consciousness the idea that, for example the exclusion of women from certain jobs, or the greater unemployment of blacks is the result either of genetically-determined behavioral or irreversible cultural patterns. These are *victim-blaming theories*. They attempt to shift the responsibility for political and economic oppression away from the dominant business and government institutions and the individuals who comprise them, and instead blame the oppression and inequality on the genetic or cultural flaws of the oppressed. This is not to say that each proponent of these victim-blaming ideologies has a direct connection with the Rockefeller family or with the Committee on Economic Development (CED), although a number of direct connections can be shown. It is to say only that the *objective effect* of these ideas is to justify and obscure the privileged position of the wealthy few in opposition to the racial, sexual, and class oppression faced by the many, by the working class.

These theories attempt to account for *real differences* in society: the lower IQs of racial minorities; the lower levels of income, health, and social services of minorities; the lower participation of women in the labor force; the greater percentage of child-rearing and domestic housework performed by women; etc. If these theories were not based on some "grain of truth," they would have no persuasive power. And, of course, racial, class, and sex differences are powder-kegs in a capitalist society. They can be the motive force for mass struggle which threatens the very foundations of this society.

94

So the differences are there. The question is: what causes them and what do they mean?

As I said above, there tend to be two versions of victim-blaming theory, of oppression-justification: the genetic version and the "cultural" version. Jensen's "hereditable IQ" and Wilson's sociobiology are recent examples of the genetic variety. Moynihan's infamous "culture of poverty" reflects the second type. There is a great deal of overlap between the two.

History of the Nutrition-Intelligence Controversy

The nutrition-intelligence hypothesis is a version of the "culture of poverty" theory. This gives me an opportunity to place this specific issue in some historical context.

There is a long history of changing attitudes toward prenatal and early infant nutrition. I will not go into this history, since some of it is beyond the scope of this talk (e.g., the breast feeding controversy). With regard to the issue of nutrition and development, the early history revolves more around the direct reproductive outcome, especially fetal wastage. In the 1930's, with the Depression, food supplements were given to women on a mass scale. During World War II in England, there was direct food rationing leading to more equal distribution of food. Pregnant working class women received more food than before, and there was an improvement in stillbirths and other indices of reproduction: other health statistics improved as well (e.g., TB mortality decreased). However, in the 1950's a number of studies yielded no conclusive evidence that prenatal malnutrition made a difference in reproductive outcome. These studies reinforced the conception of the fetus as a "perfect parasite" in symbiotic relationship with the mother. To look at it another way, the mother had enough in her own stores to supply all infant needs.

The 1960's ushered in a new experimental period. A number of researchers examined the effect of prenatal malnutrition on brain size in animals, and found a diminution in both cell size and quantity with prenatal nutritional deprivation. At the same time there began to appear some documentation of the extent of malnutrition in underdeveloped countries. It was observed, in addition, that severely malnourished children were markedly impaired. These observations taken together inspired the serious hypothesis that prenatal malnutrition around the world might be having a devastating effect on intellectual competence. By the mid-60's the popular press was writing as if the negative effect of early malnutrition on intellect was a foregone conclusion. Incidentally, in my first year of medical school, in 1972, I was taught as fact in my biochemistry class that nutritional deprivation was reducing the intelligence of children all through the underdeveloped world.

Ideological Function of the Nutrition-Intelligence Hypothesis

I will return to some of the specifics of these studies, especially some of the methodological problems, and briefly review some of the subsequent work. For now, I just wish to point out the *ideological function* of this nutrition-intelligence formulation. The 60's were a period of broad popular rebellion, around the world with the anti-imperialist movements in Southeast Asia, and in the U.S. with the Civil Rights movement and the Anti-War movement. This mass struggle focused world-wide attention on various manifestations of economic exploitation and political oppression. It was in the context of the anti-imperialist movement and the civil rights movement that victim-blaming theories, both genetic and cultural, arose. These pseudo-scientific theories attempted to account for racism or imperialism, and, at the same time, attempted to serve a function of dividing popular support from the rebelling working people in minority communities or in underdeveloped countries. One is likely to devalue the efforts of people who are seen as stupid and who are rebelling against circumstances that are, at least in part, created out of their stupidity. It is victim-blaming again. The nutrition-intelligence controversy falls, as I stated, into the camp of the "culture of poverty" theories, and, in fact, was referred to as such by authors in the 1960's.

But, of course, one must deal with truth. The proponents of these racist, sexist theories are fond of saying that while their ideas might seem to be morally repulsive, nevertheless we must face facts squarely, for it is only on the basis of truth that we can construct humane social policy. So I will examine the various arguments in the nutrition-intelligence controversy, and the evidence that has been so far amassed, so that we can see just what "truth" there is.

My overall premise is that there is no conclusive evidence that prenatal or early infant malnutrition affects intellectual ability. There is evidence, however, that nutritional deprivation can affect fetal growth and infant mortality. I will not go into any detail about this nutrition-birthweight-mortality connection, though it is certainly a socially important aspect of the role of nutrition in early human development.

Hypotheses

Let us begin by looking at various hypotheses that can be formulated to account for the relationship of early nutrition and intelligence. There are several, and these should be kept in mind as I summarize evidence. (When I speak of prenatal malnutrition, I am excluding early infant malnutrition. Most studies relate to prenatal nutritional deprivation. I will return to this important distinction later on).

1) The most common hypothesis is that prenatal malnutrition leads to diminished brain development which results in reduced mental competence.

2) A more general version of the above hypothesis has been advanced. This is that adverse prenatal experience causes a "continuum of reproductive casualty".[2] Here other prenatal insults include toxemia of pregnancy and ante-partum hemorrhage. Other resultant injuries include fetal death, cerebral palsy, mental retardation, and mild disorders of reading, speech, and behavior.

3) A contrary hypothesis was alluded to above: the developing fetus is protected, either by the placental barrier or by

metabolic compensatory mechanisms, from the adverse environment of the mother.

4) The all-or-none hypothesis: damaged fetuses die. The causal sequence is:

$$\text{adverse maternal environment} \longrightarrow \text{fetal impairment} \longrightarrow \text{fetal or early postnatal death}$$

5) Prenatal insult is overshadowed or compensated by postnatal experience. Longitudinal observation should reveal progressively diminishing prenatal contribution. There should be interaction between the prenatal insult and the quality of postnatal experience.

6) Prenatal insult differentially affects organ development. The brain is likely to be spared relative to other organs.

7) Brain growth could be reduced by prenatal insult, but such a reduction could have no effect on subsequent function.

Methodological Problems

The task now is to evaluate these various hypotheses. There are two major methodologic difficulties to keep in mind as we survey the evidence:

1) The problem of defining the independent variable, nutritional deprivation, and the dependent variable, intelligence.

2) The problem of confounding. Confounding refers to the well-known fallacy of confusing association and causation. If A causes B, and C is associated with A but has no causal relation to B, C will still be found to be associated with B. Classic examples are the increase in electricity consumption associated with the rise in lung cancer; or the association of a proliferation of stork nests with the rise in population in 19th century Europe. Given the complex of social factors surrounding under-nutrition, you can easily see that the problem of controlling potentially confounding variables is a serious one.

This problem of confounding is best examined in the context

of specific studies. Let us look at the difficulties inherent in defining the variables.

Defining and Measuring Nutritional Deprivation

Specifying nutritional deprivation has been a complex problem from several points of view. The first problem is in simply measuring what pregnant mothers eat. This is not always easy to do, even in highly controlled experiments where experimental groups are given supplements. It is possible, for example, that a woman would substitute the supplement for regular dietary constituents. Animal studies do allow the experimenter to strictly control dietary intake, but we are faced with the usual problem of generalizing from animals to humans. One approach in human studies which minimizes the uncertainty is to use an "experiment of opportunity" like the Dutch Famine, which I will speak of below, where nutritional rations are accurately measured. Even here, there was some error.

A second problem is that of specifying dietary constituents. There has been much concern with the differential effect of protein versus total calorie deprivation. Severe protein deficiency had been considered to result in Kwashiorkor; severe total calorie deficiency, in marasmus. Recently, however, the distinction has become controversial, and both syndromes are classified under the label protein-calorie malnutrition. It is still quite controversial just what dietary constituents, or how much of them, are necessary for optimum development at various stages of development.

What is more important, even if we were to ascribe some lasting developmental defects to the acute syndrome of protein-calorie malnutrition—conditions which usually result in hospitalization—this does not necessarily tell us anything about the state of "chronic under-nutrition" faced by the "hundreds of millions" of pre-school children that various authors have worried about. The effects of the acute malnutrition syndrome might be different from the effects of under-nutrition faced by much of the world's working class.

Defining and Measuring Intelligence

We now come to the problem of the dependent variable, intelligence. This problem I believe to be the central weakness in the entire culture-of-poverty/nutrition-intelligence theory. In human studies virtually all investigators have resorted to one or another of the standardized intelligence or IQ tests whether it is WISC, Raven, Stanford-Binet, etc. I will not go in depth into the whole issue of standardized tests. Suffice it to say for now that a standardized test score, or IQ, does not equal "intelligence." A variety of authors have shown in recent years that the whole standardization process of IQ tests was riddled with SES and racial biases, to the point where test developers arbitrarily assigned working class and minority subjects to lower test score groupings, or assigned lower scores to lower classes.[3, 4, 5] (This affected women until the 1930's when it was decided to standardize the test for women. This resulted in equal scores for the sexes but reduced the test's "predictive power" for future success since sexist barriers still remained in society). In other words, what IQ really measures is social class or race, without requiring intelligence as an intervening variable. Since social class is highly correlated with school performance, (with which IQ is pointed to as being highly correlated), we have the following causal sequence without "intelligence":

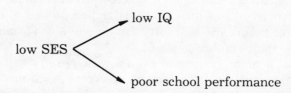

Again, the problem of confounding.

Yet dozens of authors, and countless texts and articles take these test results as indicative of "intelligence" or "learning ability," and regard lower scores as signs of lower intelligence or "cultural-familial retardation" or whatever. We all know how the Jensens and Schockleys have used lower scores among racial minorities to resurrect the same kind of racial inferiority theories that were prevalent in the early decades of this century in the U.S.*

One final point in this regard. As I said, much of the impetus for reserach in the nutrition-intelligence area was the alleged intellectual differences among social groups, particularly social classes. Among the occupational groups listed as "scoring poorly" are coal miners.[6] It could well be argued that striking miners, like those in the U.S. this year, in England a few years back, or in South Africa in the past year, have demonstrated some of the most "intelligent" behavior of anyone in their respective countries.

I should add that a few researchers have used psychomotor development tests or peer and teacher evaluation tests, but these are open to the same criticisms as the IQ tests. Also, a number of human and animal studies deal with brain size and cellular composition, but given the problem of measuring intellectual development, it is difficult to draw any functional significance from these studies. (I will return to this brain size issue). Thus we are left with the current relative inability to define, isolate and quantify the very dependent variable we are concerned with. This methodological difficulty casts a shadow on all of the research in this field.

Specific Studies

You'll remember that the basic hypothesis was that nutritional deficiency leads to organic brain damage resulting in intellectual impairment. A large body of research has dealt with the first part of this sequence, that inadequate nutritional intake leads to permanent brain damage. This research has been particularly concerned with demonstrating the existence of a *critical period*. This is the supposed period of most active brain growth, when the brain is most subject to insult and irreversible damage. Animal studies give some cre-

---

*The Nazis were very impressed with eugenics theory in the U.S., much of which drew on the early intelligence tests, and then borrowed heavily from this pseduo-scientific legacy. Jews, for example, were among the groups noted for their mental dullness by Terman and other early psychological investigators.[3]

dence to this concept of a critical period, but there are some inconsistencies. Some researchers, e.g., showed a permanent reduction in the estimated number of brain cells in rats subject to nutritional deprivation at the period of maximum brain growth.[7] (It must be remembered that different species vary in the phase of development at which the supposed maximum brain growth occurs. In rats, for example, this period is post-natal; in pigs it is pre-natal). However, some investigators could find no effects from starvation during the maximum growth period.[6]

The concept of a critical period is closely related to the concept of hyperplasia (an increase in cell number) being succeeded by hypertrophy (increase in cell size) during the process of development. Hyperplasia and hypertrophy of the two major brain cell types are the neurons, or functional cells of the nervous system, and glia, the connective tissue cells of the nervous system. Hyperplasia and hypertrophy of the two brain cell types do not occur at the same time or necessarily at the same rate. In humans an increase in the number of neurons is postulated to occur in the second trimester of pregnancy.[8] However, the maximum velocity of growth in total brain weight has been stated to occur in the months just before and after birth. In this later period, both neuronal and glial growth contribute to overall brain growth. Furthermore, the neuronal growth takes the form of hypertrophy, while the glial growth takes the form of hyperplasia. The neuronal hypertrophy which consists of the growth of various cell extensions, with dendrite and synapse formation occurs through the second year of life.[9]

Human studies of the critical period are inconclusive. Some studies of infants dying of acute malnutrition were consistent with the critical period hypothesis.[7] Infants who died in the first year of life had markedly reduced brain cell number. Those dying in the second year had no such reduction. This was interpreted to show that malnutrition during gestation or early infancy affected brain cell hyperplasia, but not later in life.

However, three problems have emerged with this kind of critical period study:

1) The critical period hypothesis rests on the idea that the functionally significant neurons are irreplaceable (though their extensions may regenerate). Now, on the one hand, the previous statement would lead us to think that the second trimester of pregnancy, when neurons proliferate, might seem to be the critical period where irreversible damage might occur. However, the third trimester, when glial cells increase in *number* and neurons in *size* is the period of maximum brain growth, and when overall fetal growth is most vulnerable to nutritional deprivation. Thus, while the third trimester fetus may be vulnerable to nutritional deprivation, it may be the second trimester that is the critical period of brain growth. During this second trimester, the nutritional needs of the fetus could be small enough for the mother to sustain the fetus under any conditions which support the mother.

2) Recent research shows that rapid brain growth may extend into the second year of life, or longer. This means that the duration of the period of starvation necessary for irreversible damage to occur has to be quite long—and in fact, it may be the postnatal period, when dendrite arborization and synaptic connections develop, that is most critical.

3) Most important: there is no good evidence that reduced total brain cell number has any functional significance.[10]

Animal Studies—Behavior

We now look at animal studies bearing on behavior per se.

There are a great number of studies in this area. While the overall results are suggestive of a nutritional effect on learning, on balance, the evidence is not conclusive. A major problem with these studies is that in experiments that expose pregnant or suckling mothers of species to under-nutrition, it is possible that the behavior of the mother could change in response to the altered social milieu, and that this in turn resulted in some of the changed behavior of the offspring. Dobbing and Smart have reviewed the evidence in this area:[11]

—Some experiments have induced delay in the development of reflexes and simple behavior patterns in rats. However, these effects could be transient, and the extension into adulthood is unclear.

—Exploratory behavior in rats nutritionally deprived in early life, was reduced on initial exposure to novel surroundings, but increased with continued exposure.

—Some starved animals learn more quickly than controls when spurred by food incentives. Possible changes in "hunger drive" complicate interpretation of animal learning experiments.

—Malnourished rats have been shown to have excessive reactions to various stressors (e.g., electric shocks, loud noises).

In summary, tests on learning are confounded by nutritional effects on other behavior. When you add the problems of generalizing from animal studies to humans, these studies become, on balance, inconclusive. We cannot tell from rats whether millions of children of the working class will be stupid. Which is not to say that animal studies are never valuable—quite the contrary—it's just that these *particular* studies are not conclusive.

Biochemical Studies

Several studies have shown alterations in myelin and cerebroside levels in the brains of deceased marasmic children (the observed deficiency in cerebroside levels is postulated to diminish dendritic arborization). Levels of norepinemphrine and epinephrine have been observed to be diminished in malnourished rats. Malnourished animals tend to have abnormally high levels of RNA-ase, indicating increased RNA breakdown. Physiological research has shown EEG abnormalities and alterations of conduction time in malnourished individuals are subjected to stress.[12,13,14]

Such studies have yielded important information on the anatomical and physiological effect of malnutrition. However, the functional significance of alterations of the various parameters is not clear.

Human Studies—Prenatal Malnutrition

There is fairly good evidence, particularly from the most recent studies [the Dutch Famine study,[6] the N.Y. Prenatal Project,[15] the Guatemala study[16]] that nutritional deprivation during pregnancy affects fertility, birthweight, and infant mortality. There seems to be a threshold effect at work. Maternal weight absorbs the first impact of nutritional deprivation. Only after a lower threshold limit of maternal weight is reached does the starvation affect the products of conception, especially placental weight. In other words, above a certain threshold value, prenatal caloric intake has little influence. I will not comment on the question of whether prenatal supplementation reduces infant mortality. The evidence does not appear to be clear, though there are some suggestive studies.[15] Suffice it to say, however, that there are other factors, besides nutritional, that affect birthweight (and infant mortality, which is closely correlated with birthweight). There are many reasons to think that we should feed mothers and children adequately, even if the contribution to birthweight and mortality is not great. There is equally great reason to conclude that we should eliminate the class and racial oppression, which embodies other causal factors in the production of low birthweight and infant mortality. In fact, if we were to eliminate such oppression, we would not have to worry about programs to supplement the diet of pregnant mothers.

There is evidence that the incidence of congenital anomalies is affected by poor prenatal malnutrition, though other social factors may be involved. Infants exposed early in gestation seem to be most affected.[6] However, congenital anomalies do not necessarily correlate with intelligence. There is some evidence that very low birthweight (less than 1500 grams) is associated with brain damage and severely reduced mental function.[17]

However, studies of mental competence with moderately low birthweight (1500 to 2500 grams) are inconclusive, and it is moderately low or normal birthweight that we are considering here. In those studies where social class was controlled for, IQ differences virtually disappear.[18] Given a close association of social class with both birthweight and IQ, what we may have is another example of social class as the overriding—and confounding—variable.

The Dutch Famine study utilized a "natural experiment," whereby for six to nine months large urban populations in the

Netherlands were suddenly deprived of food during the Nazi occupation. (You might well be disinclined to dignify fascism with any allusions to either nature or science). During the famine, fairly accurate records of caloric rations were kept. After liberation, the famine was abruptly terminated. It was thereby possible to examine fairly strictly defined cohorts of fetuses exposed to famine at various stages of development. The conclusion of this study, when looking at the IQ scores of 19 year olds registering for military induction, was that there was no demonstrable deficiency in IQ scores in those exposed to famine at various stages of development. This study did control for social class. Selective survival factors were also ruled out. That is, the all-or-none hypothesis, that damaged fetuses die, was shown not to hold. (This study did, however, legitimize the use of IQ scores).

In summary, there is no good evidence from human studies that prenatal malnutrition impairs intellectual ability. Those studies that did purport to show this, even accepting IQ as a measure of intelligence, were hopelessly confounded by other social factors associated with both malnutrition and IQ.

Postnatal Malnutrition

We are left with the problem of postnatal malnutrition, particularly given the finding of rapid brain growth in the immediate postnatal months. Several studies have dealt with this, but again the evidence is open to question because of the confounding of other social factors. Studies from South Africa,[19] Jamaica,[20] and elsewhere showed that severely malnourished children (cases) scored lower on IQ tests than controls. Once again, however, the association of malnutrition, poverty, and lower test scores was present, without a definitive causal effect of diet on IQ being isolated. Subsequent South African studies, using sibs as controls for hospitalized cases, found no test score differences.[21] However, this is not evidence against an effect of malnutrition: sibs tend to come from similar social environments, and there may be selection factors leading to hospitalization thereby rendering the cases and controls noncomparable. Such selection factors include infection leading to acute malnutrition syndrome, maternal rejection, etc. In addition, hospital admission for a control does not rule out largely common diets for both cases and controls.

The Jamaica study controlled with both siblings and matched children. Here the index cases scored lower than both sibs and matched comparison groups, with sib scores intermediate between index cases and matched comparison scores. (Similar results were reported with school behavior, as reported by teachers). This study suffers from the possibility that non-dietary experiences in childhood, associated with both lower test scores and hospitalization (that is, medical care experience) could have been different for the cases and controls. Furthermore, in comparing these two studies, there is the possibility that factors determining hospital admission could have differed in the two studies, and resulted in different test score outcomes. In fact, the Jamaican sample was largely drawn from a rural population, while the South African was drawn from an urban environment.

There are other studies, but no more definitive evidence in favor of the nutrition hypothesis.

Conclusions

Let me summarize. Famine is bad for children and other living things. I don't want to dispute that. There is evidence that nutritional deprivation has an enormous toll in fetal wastage. However, there is no conclusive evidence that under-nutrition, either pre-, post-natal, or both, causes any intellectual deficits in human beings. We have fairly safely rejected the all-or-none hypothesis, as well as the continuum of reproductive casualty hypothesis (REF-S&S), but we have not ruled out several of the other hypotheses. One of these still in the running is that the intellectual capacity of the child is protected even in conditions of severe famine.

What conclusions can we draw for this conference:

1. We should be aware of victim-blaming ideologies. It is one thing to have a hypothesis about nutrition and intelligence. It is quite another to publicize the nutrition-intelligence hypothesis as fact. We should remember the massive publicity given to the nutrition hypothesis, to the point where there are

probably many people who take this fact as a given (perhaps some of my medical school classmates).

2. We should feed children and their mothers.

3. We should struggle to eliminate the class, sex, and particularly racial differences that deprive people of decent living standards or access to employment, social services, and food.

4. This kind of research should be abandoned for the following reasons:

a. None of the indicators of the dependent variable are adequate. Studies using IQ merely legitimize an instrument that maintains the very class and race differences that perpetuate the malnutrition that is being investigated in the first place. In fact, such use of IQ devalues what could be considered the most intelligent behavior—fighting against social conditions leading to malnutrition.

b. The research is used to foster victim-blaming, racist ideas in the public mind. The nutrition-intelligence hypothesis has served as a justification for racist policies—both at home and abroad. This "theory" is particularly dangerous today in a climate of increasing government-media-sponsored hostility toward and discrimination against immigrants (undocumented workers). You can pretty quickly see how the nutrition-intelligence hypothesis would lend further "modern scientific" support to anti-immigration racism in a period marked by rising unemployment and a shrinking "pie" available for social services.

Furthermore, I believe there is a real possibility of fascism in the U.S.[22] The rise of racist and fascist groups like the Ku Klux Klan and the Nazis, the move toward greater government control in a period of economic decline, the increasing mobilization for war with the Soviet Union, the burgeoning of overt racism, sexism, brutality in the media—all these point in the direction of, and to the ruling class need for, fascism. Theories like this one "soften up" the public and only further the fascist trend.

c. The only way to have a fully controlled study would be to have a famine that lasts at least for a few years to cover cohorts ranging from gestation through the first few years of life. Such an experiment would be unthinkable (though various ruling bodies and governments are considering economic and military strategies which might foster just such an "experiment").

You could argue that this violates free speech, that people should be allowed to study what they want. In fact, there are political—or ethical—limits to social research, just as there are for all kinds of human behavior. Would we really consider acceptable the kind of medical research the Nazis engaged in; or the Tuskegee syphilis experiment; or the anthropometric studies that Jim Crow racists and Nazis engaged in. Of course not. I am arguing that this research, though not quite as blatantly racist, fascist, and sexist, can serve similar purposes.

In my view, a multi-racial struggle, of workers, students, and professionals is necessary to combat these oppression-justifying theories as well as the fascist groups like the KKK and Nazis that propagate the crudest versions of these theories. Furthermore, we need such a mass, united struggle if we are to counter the general roll-back in living and working conditions facing the working class and allied groups today and if we are to thwart the increasingly apparent trend toward war—and I mean this quite seriously. Remember, sociobiological and hereditarian theories have historically always accompanied economic decline and mobilization for war. I feel that multi-racial action is an absolute necessity for meeting what I take to be the aspirations of this conference and probably almost everyone in this room.

We should spend our intellectual and practical energies not studying the effects of hunger, but struggling to create a world where it need not exist: a world run not for profit, where, for example, agricultural workers create crops for export and barely have enough to keep themselves and their children alive, but a world run by workers for their own needs and purposes. In my own view this means that we should abandon studies like this and engage in struggle—particularly anti-racist struggle—to create a world where such studies as we have been discussing are neither necessary nor possible.

REFERENCES

1 Hansen JDL et al. What does nutritional growth retardation imply, *Pediatrics*, 47:299-311, 1971.
2 Pasamanick B. and Knobloch H. Retrospective studies of the epidemilogy of reproductive casualty, old and new. *Merrill-Palmer Quart.*, 12:7-26, 1966.
3 Thomas A. and Sillen S. in *Racism and Psychiatry*, Brunner/Mazel, New York, 1972.
4 Kagan J. What is intelligence? *Medical World*, pp. 12-14, 1973.
5 Hechinger F. M. Further proof that I.Q. data were fraudulent, *New York Times*, 1/30/79.
6 Stein Z., Susser M., Saenger G. and Marolla F. in *Famine and Human Development*, Oxford University Press, New York, 1975.
7 Winick M., Brasel J. A., and Rosso P. Nutrition and cell growth, in Winick M., ed., *Nutrition and Development*, John Wiley & Sons, New York, 1972, pp. 49-97.
8 Dobbing J. The later growth of the brain and its vulnerability. *Pediatrics*, 53:2-6, 1974.
9 Dobbing J. and Sands J. Quantitative growth and development of human brain, *Arch. Dis. Childh.*, 48:757-767, 1973.
10 Dobbing J. Malnutrition and the developing brain: a critical review. Paper given at Cornell University, Division of Nutritional Sciences, November, 1975.
11 Dobbing J. and Smart J. L. Early undernutrition, brain development and behavior, in S. A. Barnett, ed., *Clinics in Developmental Medicine, No. 47: Etiology and Development*, William Heinemann Medical Books, London, 1973.
12 Rosso P., Hormazabal, and Winick M. Changes in brain weight, cholesterol, phospholipid, and DNA content in marasmic children, *Amer. J. Clin. Nutr.*, 23:1275-1279, 1970.
13 Winick M. Malnutrition and brain development, *J. Pediatrics*, 74:667–679, 1969.

14 Coursin D. B. et al. The relationship of nutrition to brain development and behavior, *Nutrition Today*, pp. 12–17. July/Aug., 1974.

15 Susser M., Stein Z. A., and Rush D. Prenatal nutrition and subsequent development, in P. Mittler, ed., *Research to Practice in Mental Retardation:* Biomedical Aspects, Vol. III, 1977.

16 Lasky R. E. Lechtig A., and Delgado H. et al. Birthweight and psychomotor performance in rural Guatemala. *Amer. J. Dis. Child.*, 129:566, 1975.

17 Orillien C. M. The small-for-date infant: etiology and prognosis, *Pediatric Clinics of North America*, 17:9–24, 1970.

18 Record R. G., McKeown T., Edwards J. H. An investigation of the difference in measured intelligence between twins and single births. *Ann. Hum. Genet. Lond.*, 34:11–20, 1970.

19 Stoch M. B. and Smythe P. M. Does undernutrition during infancy inhibit growth and subsequent intellectual development? *Arch. Dis. Child.*, 38:546–552, 1963.

20 Richardson S. A., Birch H. G., Hertzig M. E. School performance of children who were severely malnourished in infancy, *Amer. J. Ment. Def.*, 77:623–632, 1973.

21 Evans D. E., Moodie A. D., and Hansen J. D. L. Kwashiorkor and intellectual development. *S. Afr. Med. J.*, 45:1413–1426, 1971.

22 Health Committee Against Racism. *Toward Fascism: Racism and the Destruction of Public Health*, International Committee Against Racism, November, 1979.

RACE AND SEX IN PUBLIC EDUCATION

Diane M. Morales, M.A., M.S.W.

District #3 School Board
Mid-Westside Neighborhood Health Council
New York City

As a responsible consumer of services, in this case, educational, I am asked to critique the product. I am asked to critique the product by looking at two specific aspects: the issue of race and sex in public education.

Easy, I thought. I could easily catalog a series of horrifying statistics that would unequivocally prove the failure of the educational system to educate vast numbers of minority and female children. I could easily lay the blame on boards of education for not allocating adequate resources, on teachers' unions for promoting seniority and tenure systems based on longevity rather than competency, on institutions of higher education for training teachers in irrelevant and inflexible techniques or on the educational scientific community in general for promulgating the usage of testing techniques that labelled and pigeonholed children into neat manageable categories. Not bad, I thought. But I was troubled by this almost automatic and simplistic response.

I was troubled because I could turn to any number of books, authorities, reports, etc. that had catalogued these abuses in exhaustive detail for as long as I could remember. In some instances, there had even been a reaction—a new program hailed as the answer to all these problems, a new approach, a new method. And yet as we sit here today nothing has fundamentally changed. So I decided that maybe if I did some reading I could come to grips with my gnawing and growing sense of annoyance and frustration. That effort led to further frustration. The education "mavens" only further confirmed my initial analysis: the problem is that children—particularly Black, Hispanic, Asian and female—were not benefiting from the most sophisticated public education system known in human history. In fact, they were failing in unprecedented numbers. Admittedly depending on the source, the resolution was different. Sometimes, it meant the complete overhaul of the system; at other times, it meant the introduction and integration of some innovative approach.

Last week, in a moment of mindless relaxation, I was reading a TV Guide article on why life on TV is so different from reality. The author puzzled over the television view of poor neighborhoods with "pastel drugstores, low stucco apartments with balconies overlooking artificial waterfalls, and bars with almost pitch-black interiors opening onto glaring, bright sidewalks utterly without litter or refuse. "Where is this world?" he wondered. After he moved to Los Angeles, he recognized that TV producers and writers were simply reflecting the world they live in—the super-clean, super-bright world of Los Angeles, where even the slums are spotless and have palm trees in front. Interesting, I thought. Could this same argument hold true for the education system? Could public education in the United States be a reflection of the larger society? But, of course, that's it. But, wait a moment, there is another piece. It isn't only a reflection but it is also the keeper of the flame. Education passes on to the next generation all those things that human endeavor has created, fought for, cherished and valued and a part of that package is racism and sexism.

I don't pretend to speak from the vantage point of great scholarly research or extensive study. I only can speak from the vantage point of that unique experience of being one of a minority within a minority—a Puerto Rican woman who survived the New York City public school system. The mere fact that I view my educational experience as a matter of survival is, in and of itself, the greatest indictment of that system that I can think of.

I entered the New York City public school system at the age of six, speaking my native tongue, Spanish. I learned English as many Puerto Rican children in New York schools in the 1950's did, in a CRMD class—a class for children of retarded mental development. I was given an IQ test and scored a 78—marginal at best. Maybe, I was told, I could learn a trade; I surely couldn't be allowed to take the test for a specialized high school, although I wanted to. But somehow I managed to graduate the eighth grade as class valedictorian and repeated that achievement upon graduation from high school. Having escaped the label of retarded mental development, I was pigeonholed as exceptional, an overachiever. And since I was one of a very few, I could be tolerated by the system and assimilated. I could be made to conform to the reality of education in this country: the majority of Blacks, Hispanics do not succeed in school—but there are exceptions.

So, what is educational reality in the United States? Colin Greer[1] in the *Great School Legend* states it like this:

> "America is a very conservative society which likes to claim that it is devoted to equality and social change. It has a public school system designed to preserve that contradiction—by institutionalizing the rhetoric of change to preserve social status."

In my own words it is the reality of a society which reaches with almost infantile greediness for easy answers, facile justifications and euphemisms to perpetuate the *status quo*. It is a reality of white middle class male educators who were raised in a world dominated by white middle class men. I had thought that I would come here today to ask for a re-examination of this reality. But I am not. I had thought that I would ask the educators, the teachers, the scientists to look at the theories, tests, the programs they have created and evaluate them in light of new evidence of erroneous data and racist and sexist thinking. But I am not.

No, I only have one small request. Let us all agree to recognize that education is just one of the institutions (and perhaps the most powerful) of a society which promotes and sustains racism and sexism as a fundamental tenet of economic control.

Let us look at some of the evidence: In January, 1977 the Office of Civil Rights, Department of Health, Education and

114

Welfare, cited the New York City Public School system in violation of Title VI of the Civil Rights Act of 1964 which prohibits discrimination on the basis of race, color and national origin, Title IX of the Education Amendments of 1972 which prohibits discrimination on the basis of sex and Section 504 of the Rehabilitation Act of 1973 which prohibits discrimination against physically or mentally handicapped individuals. The specifics of this citation were as follows:

(1) On the basis of race, national origin, sex and physical and mental handicap, New York City public schools deprived minority, female and handicapped students of an equal share of the resources provided from local tax revenues for basic education by (a) allocating lower per pupil instructional expenditures for the education of minority students, (b) providing more limited and poorer quality facilities and educational materials for their education, (c) establishing a more limited and less desirable range of curricula and instructional and non-instructional programs, and (d) assigning less experienced and less well-qualified staff to provide instruction; and denied minority students the full benefits of special supplementary education programs provided from Federal sources intended solely for the benefit of educationally disadvantaged students, by diverting such funds to other uses.

(2) On the basis of race and national origin, denied minority students meaningful educational experience and the full benefits of educational programs offered by segregating minority students in educationally disadvantaging instructional settings where they are subjected to restricted curricular opportunities and inferior instructional services and by providing inappropriate instructional approaches for students with primary language abilities in languages other than English.

(3) On the basis of race, national origin and sex, denied minority and female students access to the full range of educational opportunities afforded other students by (a) providing a lower level of guidance and counseling assistance in terms of the opportunity for and access to services, and the type, duration and quality of such services, (b) restricting the ability of students to participate in academic and specialized curricula; and (c) guiding and channeling these students to-

ward classes, tracks of overall educational, economic and career objectives which are more restricted in range and often race and sex stereotyped.

(4) On the basis of race and national origin, subjected minority students to disciplinary practices which have resulted in harsher punishments (both in terms of type and duration) being meted out to minority as compared to nonminority students, both in general and for the same offense, through the application of vague and subjective criteria.

The report continues with an exhaustive detailing of each specific charge with documentary and statistical evidence supporting each charge. To date the New York City public school system remains in virtually the same position. The Central Board of Education has spent most of two years since the release of the report denying it, finding excuses for the existence of such situations, and generally hoping (and I suspect not in vain) that the report will wend its way to some dusty shelf.

But the Office of Civil Rights report is only a part of the evidence. This report doesn't deal with a white-controlled Community School Board that turns down funds that would have employed minority students in work-study projects. It doesn't touch the charges of reverse discrimination when a Black superintendent denies tenure to a white supervisor. It doesn't reach the issue of a white parent requesting a transfer for her child because she/he is the only white child in his/her class and therefore is denied peer group intellectual stimulation. It doesn't impact on the 7th grade Puerto Rican female reading on a 4th grade level programmed for 7 periods of typing and 6 periods of physical education and no remedial reading in the course of a school week. It doesn't deal with the out-of-school 15 year-old Black student who is 4 months pregnant and is told that she is on a waiting list 6 months long for admittance to a school for pregnant girls.

That is evidence. It is undeniable, pervasive and compelling. It speaks to programmed failure by class, by sex and by race. Colin Greer[1] states it this way: "The fact of the matter is that American public schools in general, and urban public schools in particular, are a highly successful enterprise. Basic

116

to that success is the high degree of academic failure among students. Attitudes and behavior patterns such as tolerance of boredom, learning as memorization, competition and hostility are learned and reinforced in the classroom. The schools do the job today that they have always done. They select out individuals for opportunities according to a hierarchial schema which runs closely parallel to existing social class patterns . . . the school system, then, stands as an institutional statement of public morality, providing a set of defensive guarantees for the protection of the various orders of society."

So what are the answers, where are the solutions? It doesn't seem reasonable to expect that the reformation of the public education system in this country without a *concomitant* reformation and redistribution of social and economic power will yield any lasting effects. Mine is a very personal and probably not very profound beginning of a solution. It deals with the stripping away of euphemisms. The country is beguiled by euphemisms—you've heard them all—socially maladjusted, culture of poverty, emotionally handicapped, planned shrinkage, benign neglect. They have all been used as *apologies* for racism, sexism and classism. They have been used to beguile, divert and subvert. As women, as Hispanics, as Blacks we have accepted them and at times even used them. Let's recognize them for what they truly are: euphemisms that label, that stigmatize and pigeonhole. Euphemisms that stripped away reveal the true nature of this society.

REFERENCES

[1] Greer, Colin. *The Great School Legend.* Penguin Books, New York, 1972.

EDUCATION AND THE NATIVE AMERICAN CHILD

Donna Lovell

Native American Education Program
New York City

I learned only one lesson during elementary school with reference to the American Indian. In seventh grade, our social studies teacher made sure that we understood the importance of the Iroquois in New York by assigning us the task of drawing a map of the state. Included were the locations of the five original nations of the Iroquois Confederacy, their functions in the League, and the Montauk nations of Long Island. I still have that map and use it in teaching my Native American history class. I will always remember and give credit to my seventh grade teacher for creating a spark of interest in me that led to a career in Indian education.

My childhood was often spent wondering about my grandfather's people, the Blackfoot. Unfortunately, he died before I realized how important his knowledge would have been to me and my children. But I grew up in a family that stressed education. And my education did not include the histories and cultures of Native American peoples. American Indians were the "noble savages," forever implanted in the American memory of the old west. They had been conquered to insure the progress of the great United States; to make way for the settlement and development of the land. My fellow classmates and I were told that the only real Indians lived on reservations west of the Mississippi, and that they were the vanishing race. In light of the popular thought at that time, it was very difficult for me to establish my Indian heritage as valid and relevant. I was very proud to let people know that I was Blackfoot but gradually became confused and angry when the terms heathen and savage were jokingly used. But you see, their connotations did not really apply to me because teachers and friends always explained that I wasn't a "real Indian."

However, as the years went by, I sought to teach myself that which was omitted from my history books. My mother, uncle, aunts, and grandmother became my information sources, even though their knowledge was limited. My classes in college became especially arduous due to the complete invisibility of the Native American in history, philosophy, and literature. Therefore, whenever possible, I always studied the subject matter from the Native American viewpoint. In all of my American history classes, I prepared a term paper on various aspects of Native American history which coincided with the time period we were studying. In my European philosophy notebook, I compared Nietzsche's world view with that of Castaneda's Don Juan. I enjoyed writing papers about literature that I had read by or about Native Americans. My professors often learned from my efforts and continually encouraged me.

In 1976, immediately after graduation from the City College of New York, I began working for an Indian Education program in New York City. Technically known as Title IV, part A, this particular project is funded under the Indian Education Act of 1972, through the Office of Indian Education, Washington, D.C. Part A of Title IV is a nation-wide plan, designed to handle the special educational and cultural needs of American Indian children who attend public schools. Part B is for students in parochial schools and Part C provides for the education of Native American adults. Our funding is administered by the Board of Education of New York City.

The Native American Education Program (Part A) services Native American children attending kindergarten through twelfth grade in all of the five boroughs. We provide tutorial services, history and culture classes, and also maintain a resource center, which houses books, tapes, films, periodicals and records for use by program participants. We also provide a home/school visitation service where liaisons visit public schools to identify Native American students and introduce our program to them.

120

The very existence of Title IV is in itself a definite improvement in the awareness of the need for better educational methods and learning materials for Native Americans. However, insidious misinformation about the American Indian perpetuated through literature, the media, and insensitive individuals and educators continues to be our greatest obstacle. It has been most difficult to combat and correct ideas and value judgments that are so deeply ingrained in society's view of the American Indian. The situation, I'm sorry to admit, has not really changed too greatly since my experience in school. The reeducation of the dominant society toward Native Americans has been slow indeed.

The children who are eligible for this program are constantly bombarded with stereotypes presented by curriculum, teachers, television and friends that often lead to serious identity problems. In order to successfully avoid snide comments and offensive ridicule, many Native American children will identify with an ethnic group other than their own to gain acceptance among peers. When our staff goes into a school to do a presentation, we're very careful not to use a Native American child in the class as an example. The child will usually decide during or at the end of the presentation whether or not to become known to us and consequently to the rest of the class. Since our classroom lectures focus on personal pride and experiences and accurate, undistorted history, many children upon hearing a positive reinforcement of their heritage and culture will approach us and say that they are Indian.

We also explain to our students that the amount of "Indian blood" has no relevance in determining their Indianness. This is due to the fact that society has placed such a false importance on being "full blood." Children often feel that if they're not full bloods, they're not "real Indians." Our staff is very candid in stating that blood quantum is a device used by the government to continuously divide and conquer our people. We tell them that intermarriage between Native Americans and various ethnic groups was necessary for survival; that they should be proud of all that they are.

The staff of the Native American Education Program has

been very successful in enlightening many individuals in and around New York City on various aspects of Native American history and culture. Our greatest dilemma is that we have not reached enough people. The size of New York City alone makes our job almost impossible. There are one thousand schools in the five borough area with an enrollment of about one million pupils. According to the census of 1970, there are at least 10,000 Native Americans residing in New York City. In identifying the Indian students, we must rely on an ethnic survey which is conducted annually by the Board of Education. Last year, the survey reported over seven hundred Indian students. This year, there are less than five hundred. The survey is usually done by sight and at one time was not turned in by every district. Needless to say, the figures are erroneous; we believe them to be a misrepresentation of the true number.

Another major concern of our organization is to sensitize educators to recognize stereotypes and misinformation in children's literature, textbooks, and existing resource materials that are used in the classroom. Too often, teachers will be taken in by seemingly innocuous materials either because the teachers are honestly unaware of the true facts, or they don't understand the insinuations. As a result, the information learned in school does very little to successfully counteract the plethora of misinformation which is disseminated about Native Americans outside the classroom. Too often, in reviewing curricular materials used in city public schools, I find that American history still begins with Columbus' discovery of America. World history is continuously presented from a white European perspective, with little or no attention given to the Native American viewpoint.

Children's books are great offenders in promoting Native American stereotypes. Indian children see themselves listed in alphabet books along with Inkwells and Insects. Native Americans "lurk" behind bushes, have red skin, and always wear feathers. Animals are depicted wearing headdresses with names like Chief Running Bear. The examples are endless and equally depressing.

Two years ago, our staff, in cooperation with the Council

122

on Interracial Books for Children recorded the comments and reactions of Native American children as they skimmed through literature illustrating the aforementioned stereotypes. The result was the creation of a filmstrip entitled, "Unlearning Indian Stereotypes." The filmstrip has been well received by instructors from different areas of the country. It is an invaluable learning tool for elementary school teachers. Instructors should be sensitized and trained to develop new and innovative ideas in teaching about Native Americans. They should also begin to understand and place in proper perspective traditional Native American values, religion, and language. If instructors can perceive and relate the impact of these factors on an Indian child attending a school that is not a traditional Native American school, then methods can be carefully developed to help improve the child's academic performance.

In every treaty made with the United States government, the education of our children was promised to us. But the educational system in the United States has not only failed Indian children, but all children. Solutions to the problem of education in this country will hopefully be found in the very Native American traditions and values that the dominant society ignores.

As more Native Americans graduate from college and enter the field of education, more research will be conducted; better materials will be developed and distributed. Progress is being made with self-determination as our goal. For the moment the future of Indian education looks promising.

CHILDREN: THE VICTIMS OF RACIST BIAS IN SCIENCE

Dorothy C. Burnham

Empire State College

For today's meeting which is held as a part of the observance of the International Year of the Child, I should like to take a look at the role which some scientists have played in contributing to the racist ideology which determines a good part of the life circumstances of the Black and minority child in America. For scientists, artists, workers and professionals producing in a racist cultural milieu respond and react as a part of that environment and the biases of racism influence thinking, observations, theories and activities to a degree not often fully recognized or acknowledged. Scientists, like other workers, absorb the ideas and attitudes of the racist society and frequently convey racist theories back to the community as a part of their 'scientific' research. Few take into consideration the fact that the dynamics of this feed back operation interferes severely with scientific objectivity.

Dr. Richard Lewontin, in a paper published last year in *Biology as a Social Weapon,* examines the history of the natural scientists' contribution to the ideologies of racism, class superiority and sexism.[1] He outlines with clarity and understanding how ideas have been used to sustain the class biased, white and male supremacist society. From skull measurements to IQ tests, from blood inheritance to genetic chemistry and neurophysiology, experiments have been conducted, observations made, interpretations published, all supportive of the ideas of the innate superiority of white upper and middle class children over Black, minority and poor children.

Earlier scientific and medical studies which claimed to support the idea of Black inferiority appear ludicrous and crude today. Kenneth Stampp writing about the medical profession during slavery said, "Another sign of southern medicine was the common (though not universal) belief that the physical and emotional differences between Negroes and Caucasians were too great to permit the same medical treatment for both races." He quotes from a noted Louisiana physician who says, "The Negro is sensual rather than intellectual . . . The seat of Negro consumption is not in the lungs but in the mind."[2] The dissemination of ideas like these among the American people helped them to accept the buying and selling of Afro-American children and the breeding of Black children for the slave market. The continuing acceptance of the racist ideology based on the alleged biological inferiority of Black children helped in no small measure to maintain the establishment of segregation, discrimination and the ghettoizing of Black and minority families long after the abolition of slavery.

Scientific and technological advances have changed the material world in which our children are growing up. Advances in medicine have helped to reduce the overall mortality rate from 99 per thousand in 1915 to 15.1 per thousand in 1976.[3] That the infant mortality rate among minority children is 23.5 per thousand in 1976[4] demonstrates that the benefits of science have been far from equally divided. These figures reflect the toll that poverty and racism takes on the minority child.

In the urban centers there has been a serious increase in malnutrition. Four times as many Black and minority children die from malnutrition and avitaminosis every year than do white children of the same age.[5] Inflation has taken out of the pockets of the poor the money needed to feed the children. With milk, fruit, meat—the necessities for growth—selling at record prices, many children are going without essential foods day after day. And too many children go hungry.

The 1959 Declaration of the Rights of the Child reaffirmed the principle of the right of all children to educational opportunity. The struggle for an education has been a constant struggle ever since Afro-Americans were brought in chains to this country. The year of our meeting marks the 25th Anniversary of the Brown decision in which the Supreme Court

125

ruled unanimously that segregated schools were inherently unequal. Yet a retrospective article in the New York Times indicates that in the major urban centers of America—Detroit, Chicago, Philadelphia, Houston, New York and Los Angeles—the number of children attending segregated schools had increased dramatically since 1957.[6] Twenty-five years after its commitment to desegregation the government tolerates open defiance of the law and opposition ranges from subtle tactics to the open encouragement of racist mobs and the Ku Klux Klan as in Boston, to harass our children who seek their right to an education.

In 1901, Dr. DuBois said at the sixth Atlanta Conference, "We are deliberately raising millions of our citizens in ignorance and at the same time limiting the rights of citizenship by educational qualifications."[7] It is sad that 75 years later this statement is still valid.

And instead of the society trying to solve the problems of undereducation of a large percentage of children, we find the research scientists directing their studies to prove that the reasons for the poor educational results are innate and inherited and the fault of the victim rather than the responsibility of society. They invade our schools, testing and retesting the children rather than teaching, and the media give great publicity to the findings that Blacks are unequipped for higher learning.

In August of 1978, The American Psychological Association met in Toronto. There was a week of meetings and several hundred papers were presented. *Science News* selected two for feature stories. One feature was a report on a paper presented by Arthur R. Jensen, titled by *Science News:* "Jensen: Intelligence a 'biological rhythm'".[8] On a continuing crusade to justify his earlier research contentions linking IQ, heredity and race, Jensen now claims to have discovered a "g" factor measuring reaction time and relating this to intelligence. He asserts the "g" factor has a definite "biological basis." And he told the *Science News* reporter: "I think there is a genetic basis—it would be impossible to argue otherwise."

To those of you who are familiar with Jensen's work, it

should come as no surprise that he claims to have found at the junior college level that Blacks exhibited slower reaction time than whites. This is the man who at every confrontation asserts his non-biased objectivity. Yet he has chosen as his main area of research the task of showing the intellectual inferiority of Black children. We note that although geneticists, psychologists and other scientists have pointed to the fallacies in his work, Jensen apparently finds financial resources, a platform and media support.

The social sequelae of racism, poverty, illness, poor housing and nutrition have had sometimes disastrous effects upon our children. It is discouraging to find social and psychological scientists proposing biological solutions to these problems.

The second feature article from the APA meeting reported in *Science News* was headlined. "Delinquency as a Learning Disability."[9] The author, Allan Berman, a professor at the University of Rhode Island focuses on neuropsychological dysfunction and speculates that subtle brain deficiencies in children may be responsible for triggering delinquent behavior years later. Berman says, "We think we can predict high risk children in the third grade." *Science News* points out that Berman does not propose drugs or surgical treatment. Earlier researchers in this area had been severely criticized for proposing brain surgery for "deficient" brain mechanisms. This particular study was made on both delinquent boys serving their first sentence at a Rhode Island correctional facility, and on students from an inner city school.

This research scientist, like others in his field, may recognize the social, political and economic causes of anti-social behavior among children, but his orientation leads him to look at the individual child to discover innate mechanisms which can be switched on or off to alter anti-social behavior. Working from this premise, many Black children have been victimized in behavior modification programs by careless and unwarranted drug administration and by the cruel and unusual punishment called euphemistically avoidance therapy. The numbers of Black and minority children so mistreated is proportionately larger because subjects for the programs and research are more frequently chosen from inner city schools which are predominantly Black and from the city and county hospitals which serve the poor.

Scientists are not equally responsible for the promotion of racist scientific research. Many are aware of the dangers of lending a cover of scientific objectivity to clearly biased research. Many have played a leading role in uncovering the fallacies, the unsound research practices in much of the work. Further they have taken the necessary political steps, going beyond academic halls to picket lines and other effective demonstrations. These men and women deserve the support of all of us who are interested in the welfare of children.

Marion Wright Edelman, Director of the Children's Defense Fund, says, "We must organize. Groups and individuals working on behalf of children must stop fighting each other and begin to build political networks across this country to educate the public and prod policy makers to do what is necessary for our children. We can no longer delude ourselves that children are above politics. Their lives are deeply affected by political decisions, and we must become as effective as others who wield political clout."[10]

Ms. Edelman points out that we cannot think of children's rights as above politics. In the same vein, we cannot think of scientists as being beyond politics. Their work and research has political and social implications for our children. We therefore have to alert ourselves to and discuss the political methods we need to develop to halt scientific research which supports and abets racism.

REFERENCES

1 Lewontin, Richard C., "Biological Determinism as a Social Weapon", In Ann Arbor Science for the People Editorial Collective, *Biology as a Social Weapon.* Burgess Publishing Company, Minneapolis, Minnesota, pp. 6–18, 1977.

2 Stampp, Kenneth, *The Peculiar Institution: Slavery in the Ante-Bellum South,* Vintage Paper Edition, New York. pp. 308, 309. 1956.

3 *Statistical Abstracts of the United States,* Washington,D.C., United States Government Printing Office. pp. 55, 1977.

4 *Vital Statistics of the United States,* 1976, Volume II, Mortality Part B. p. 7, Section 7–Table 7, 2.

5 *Vital Statistics of the United States,* 1973, Volume II, Part A, Section I—General Mortality, Table 1–8. pp. 1–14.

6 Reinhold, Robert, "25 Years After Desegregation North's Schools Lag", *New York Times,* pp. A1, B11, May 17, 1979.

7 DuBois, William Edward Burghardt, Washington, Booker T. and others, in *The Negro Problem,* James Pott and Company, New York. pp. 64, 65. 1903.

8 Jensen, A., "Intelligence A Biological Rhythm", *Science News,* Volume 114, No. 11, p. 181. 1978.

9 Berman, A., "Delinquency as a Learning Disability", *Science News,* Volume 114, No. 11, p. 180. 1978.

10 Edelman, Marian Wright, "Develop a National Agenda for Children" article commissioned by Association for Childhood Education International, The National Association for the Education of Young Children and the United States National Committee for Early Childhood Education for publication during the International Year of the Child, 1979.

129

GENDER, MINORITY STATUS AND EDUCATIONAL INSTITUTIONS

Edmund W. Gordon, Ed. D.

Professor of Psychology and Afro-American Studies Yale University

The history of modern societies has been marked by recurrent efforts at broadening the populations to which special privilege is assigned, or better, at reducing the populations who are deprived of opportunities that others are afforded. This trend in the development of human societies is probably best marked by the recurrent efforts at the redistribution of wealth; the movement has been slow but consistent in the direction of broadening the group of persons who either own wealth or at least share in the benefits of wealth through income. Although it doesn't explain all revolutions, some of the great revolutions of history have had the redistribution of wealth at their core.

The second thrust has been the effort at broadening political participation, that is, increasing the number and variety of persons who participate in political decision-making. Here we can go back to the early efforts of tribal groups at elevating the elders of the community to positions of power and decision-making, thus tempering the total autonomy of the chief; or to the major political revolutions in history where the effort has been to enfranchise a larger proportion of the population. In very recent periods political participation by women and later by Blacks has been at the core of the struggles to broaden political participation in general.

Similar trends can be seen in the effort to increase the number of persons who read and interpret the Scriptures. In fact, one of the central issues involved in the Protestant Reformation was the right to read the Scriptures and to interpret them for oneself, freeing persons from those interpretations that were meted out to them by the clergy. This effort at increasing the body and number of literate persons, persons who could read, was also stimulated by the expanding needs of industrializing societies for literate workers, that is, workers who could read directions and participate on a minimal level in the commerce of the community. These efforts were not, however, limited to the reading of the Scriptures or directions for limited travel, but came to be expressed in increased demands for participation in public policy determination. Thus, in the United States, a new system of government based on almost universal participation in public policy determination, that is, the participation of all property owners, originally, and subsequently the participation by all citizens, came to be the rule. Once these democratic forces had been set in motion, what we had were increasing efforts at obtaining civil rights for all persons in the society, and, again, it was initially for all males and later for women. When the Women's Suffrage movement combined with the antislavery movement and the abolitionist movement, what we were about was obtaining civil rights for all people, and, of course, expanding those rights to insure the protection of the rights and liberties of women and a number of ethnic minorities in the society.

In the most recent years, that is from the mid-nineteen-fifties, attention has focused most heavily on insuring equal rights to ethnic minorities, the rights of persons of the dominant minority ethnic groups in the society, to the use of public facilities, to equal education, and to equal job opportunities. Since the assertion of rights by one group tends to stimulate the assertion of rights by others, what we have also seen in this recent period is a variety of groups asserting their claim to be treated more fairly by society. Even more recently, we have seen a back-and-forth shift in the priority given to each of these groups.

Attention has recently been focused on the rights of several specific ethnic minorities, the rights of women, the rights of persons of less typical sex identifications, the rights of non-standard-English speakers and the rights of the handicapped. Since modern societies seem to have difficulty focusing comprehensively on all related problems or even on a single problem for any appreciable length of time, we seem to flip back and forth, giving priority to one of these problems today and another tomorrow. We sometimes find the categorical proponents of these issues competing. Some members of the Black movement feel threatened by the women's movement. Some members of the women's movement feel threatened by the Black movement, and either one may feel threatened by the growth of the gay movement, and all of these are now worried about the movements of the handicapped and non-standard-English-speaking groups. As we look cautiously over our shoulders at one another, the forces that would do us all in are applauding our conflicts and continuing their exploitation of all these low status groups. Obviously the struggle is not for the rights of women or Blacks or Native Americans or handicapped persons; the struggle is for the protection of the human rights of all persons and of all groups of persons.

In my view there are three fundamental impediments to the achievement of such protection for all. The first is the exploitative and reactionary political economy by which resources and power are controlled. The second is constrictive and distorting ignorance and misinformation. The third is the restrictive and recalcitrant attitudes and behaviors born of the influences of the former two. Let us discuss each briefly.

Behind most efforts at discrimination or the assertion of privilege for an isolated group is a concern with more greatly protecting the security of the group which is asserting privilege. Unfortunately, as societies become more complex, it is more and more difficult to establish security for oneself without exploiting another, so that if we look at the richer and poorer nations of the world, or the privileged and less privileged ethnic groups in society, or the privilege that men in our society have over women, one of the underlying factors is the concern that the privileged group has with securing and controlling and subsequently, with protecting its control of resources and power. Since it is not sufficiently protective of my feeling of security with respect to resources that I be supplied for today and maybe one day ahead, I must supply myself for the indefinite future. To create this imaginary or real surplus reserve, I must depend upon the work, the talents, the co-operation, and the ignorance of other people. When one individual or group claims ownership of that reserve that is what I call exploitation. Alongside exploitation, of course, is the control of the economic and political decision-making in the society, in ways that permit me to maintain those economic relationships that have served my best interests. In this way, a conservative approach to the status quo gets exaggerated into what we call a reactionary approach, where spokespersons for privileged groups go to extreme ends to control the political process, since the political process so greatly determines the nature of the economic processes. So underlying the competition or the continuing practice of group discrimination is this exaggerated concern for security, expressed in our society as economic security; the concern for the protection of that economic security and privilege is expressed through control of the political processes of the country, with primary attention on maintaining existing relationships. Obviously, if the positions of the lower-status people are to be changed, both exploitation and conservatism, or reactionary conservatism, must be done away with.

The second impediment is the constrictive and distorting ignorance or misinformation that dominates the society. Again, if one looks at the history of the disenfranchisement of blacks and the disenfranchisement of women, these efforts have always run corollary to major efforts at demeaning the status, the confidence, and the potentials of these groups, so that conceptions of superiority and inferiority get promulgated. Since they are promulgated by the same forces that are concerned primarily with maintaining exploitative advantage and privileged positions, the information which is made available must necessarily serve that purpose; this means that facts relating to sex differences or to ethnic differences are distorted in ways that either pit groups against one another, or at least justify the inferior position to which the low-status group has been assigned and in which it is held. It is not surprising that black people will be served less well by a society that believes they are less capable of functioning in that society, or that women will have less opportunities in a society

133

that believes they are less capable than other members of the society of performing in, or serving, that society. This constrictive force operating on the opportunity structure for low-status persons can be modified only if the ideas that people hold are changed. One of the things that we should thus be concerned with in a conference such as our meeting today is providing the kind of correct information, or at least more balanced information, that can challenge some of the distortions that have been passed on as fact, in this instance with respect to differences in sex and gender.

Going hand in hand with ignorance and misinformation are restrictive and recalcitrant attitudes and behaviors, that is, attitudes and behaviors that restrict the opportunity of others; attitudes and practices that are so fixed that they dominate the thinking and behaviors of large numbers of persons. When we begin to think, though, about the ways in which attitudes get changed, we run into rather complicated processes. There is still considerable debate in the behavioral sciences with respect to whether we change attitudes and expect people's behaviors to follow, or whether we change the behaviors and expect the attitudes to follow. My own bias is in the direction of the latter. We can create experiences by which low-status people are provided the opportunity to function in society as other people do, and high-status people are precluded from discriminating against or abusing or exploiting low-status persons; to the extent that those conditions effectively prevail, and members have different and wholesome experiences in the new condition, the changed behaviors of persons will eventually result in changed attitudes.

I recognize, though, that this area of attitude change is probably the most difficult of our problems. It is considerably easier to pass laws that reduce, if they do not eliminate, exploitation and reactionary domination of politics. It is certainly possible to provide the information and educational experiences that have the potential for counteracting constrictive and distorting ignorance. But when it comes to the changing of attitudes that so much of a person's experience supports, we have a problem that requires the concerted efforts of all of the institutions in the society. These institutions need information resources in order to change the opportunity structure and ultimately to change the prejudicial attitudes. There is a need to influence the policy decisions by which the society regulates an individual's opportunities and to influence the social processes by which persons of different gender identities, ethnic identities, and class identities are rewarded. Those activities that are necessary to effect changes in the way the system works become an important aspect of those activities of ours which are directed at effecting changes in people's attitudes.

In working on these three levels of problems, we are not talking about what we do for women or what we do for Puerto Ricans or what we do for Blacks. We should be talking about what we do for people, because it is in the competition among these several groups that we find insufficient attention being given to these underlying factors. It is almost as if the society would encourage intergroup struggle in order to distract us from the problems that are common to all these groups.

So far we have talked primarily about the sociopolitical context, in which differences in sex and gender as well as a number of other status differences must be considered. It is important that we understand why we have chosen to focus on both sex and gender as conceptual frames. We take the position that when we talk about sex differences, we are talking about biological differences in the structure and functioning of persons. When we talk about gender differences, we are talking about the social role differences, differences in the roles people learn to play or are forced to fill. Sex differences are important, and, in some instances, highly obvious, but there are very few ways in which differences that adhere to biological sex limit the functioning and participation of the representatives of the two sexes. It is when we turn to differences in gender, that is, differences in the roles assigned to and imposed upon men and women in our society, that we find our greatest contributors to differences in opportunity, differences in the availability of resources, and differences in attitudes, treatments, and rewards. In other words, there are very few things that women cannot do simply because they are female, just as there are very few things that men cannot

135

do simply because they are male, but there are many things that women have less opportunity to do, or that men, for that matter, are less rewarded for doing as a result of their gender.

We need the knowledge base by which we may better understand these differences, be they biological or sociopsychological. Underlying all of these concerns, of course, is our concern with the implications that this knowledge has for educational treatment and social opportunity.

EDUCATIONAL IMPLICATIONS
OF GENES AND GENDER

Vera John-Steiner, Ph.D.

University of New Mexico

The powerful role of beliefs in the exploration of "human nature" and how these beliefs affect children is the topic of my presentation today. I agree with Leon Eisenberg, who wrote in 1972 that "what we believe of man affects the behavior of men, for it determines what each expects of the other. Theories of education, of economics, and the very policies of the government are based on implicit concepts of the nature of human beings."[1]

The need to examine such implicit concepts is clear to many women, as the depiction of the female sex in some of the most influential theories has been biased—for instance, in those of Freud and Jung. There is further concern among women at present (see previous volumes of *Genes and Gender*) because theorists committed to biologically deterministic models of human behavior are growing in numbers and in decision-making powers. Their influence is strong among those educators who prefer to explain the crisis in public education, particularly the failure in adequately schooling poor and minority children, by invoking heredity instead of the limitations of current school practices.

Thus, the appeal of an ideology which ascribes socially-produced inequality among learners to genetic causes is linked to the recurrent and unresolved issues of equity. The mismatch between what schools need to accomplish in a technologically demanding society and what they in fact are accomplishing has resulted in more and more criticisms leveled against them. Funds have become scarce for innovation and educational research, and many teachers fear losing their jobs. In the face of what appears to be a hopeless situation, some educators are opting for a view of teaching and learning which exempts them from responsibility.

It is in this context that E. O. Wilson's sociobiological notions, particularly the emphasis in his theory upon biologically-imposed constraints upon human adaptability, have gained adherents. The widespread publicity Wilson and others have received in the mass media has further contributed to the impact of sociobiology upon educators and social scientists. Stephen Jay Gould points out that such popularity in the press is not a new phenomenon. He writes that "The protracted and intense debate surrounding biological determinism has arisen as a function of its social and political message. . . . biological determinism has always been used to defend existing social arrangements as biologically inevitable—from 'ye have the poor always with you' to nineteenth century imperialism to modern sexism. Why else should a set of ideas so devoid of factual support gain such a consistently good press from established media throughout the centuries?"[2]

There is an important historical connection between theories used against the poor, against colonized people and women, as pointed out by Gould. My emphasis in this paper is a similar one; I see the role of biologically deterministic theories as a traditional weapon against all of these groups.

The readers of popular magazines are not familiar with the strong and informed opposition to these theories voiced by a large group of behavioral scientists. Some of their statements have been collected in A. L. Caplan's *The Sociobiological Debate*; others have been published in the previous volumes of this series. One of the central assumptions of those who are committed to an egalitarian position in the debates concerning human nature is that *socially-acquired* characteristics of humans govern the fine interplay between the continuities and changes in human life.

The role of social forces in shaping children's interest in and preparation for successful educational achievement has been widely stressed in the past. But frequently the view of what social and cultural forces consist of has been narrowly conceived. A broader view is presented by Anthony Quinton: "Our social and cultural heritage is not biparental: in this respect we are the direct heirs of all ages. We can acquire knowledge, technique, values and institutions from anyone, anywhere, at any time by the simple act of verbal communication."[3]

Although Quinton may underestimate the complexity of the learning process, however, he is in agreement with many others in the field who stress the great plasticity of the human organism. All egalitarian theorists refute the simplistic notion that there are specific genes which determine specific behavioral traits, or as Tobach writes: "The reduction of explanation to genetic function is basically the key to the weakness of Wilson's extrapolation of the postulates of sociobiology to all levels of social organization".[4] The biological potential of human beings consists in our ability to modify our existence, or as David Hawkins puts it "to be the inventor, transmitter and receiver of the fruits of cultural evolution."[5]

Tobach, Hawkins, and Quinton join many other scientists who view the nature-nurture controversy from the point of view of a *dynamic interactionist* stance. A full account of the assumptions and the methods implicit in this approach is beyond the scope of this paper. Indeed, at present, such an integrated theory which cuts across a number of disciplines is still to be accomplished. But it is possible to identify social scientists who do not subscribe to either nativist, behaviorist, Freudian or Piagetian concepts, and who have proposed new approaches to some of the most crucial issues within their disciplines using an interactionist framework.

These theorists share a determination to overcome the simple dichotomy of "Nature" and "Culture" and to replace these, and similar polarities, through the exploration of the full range of reciprocal interactions which characterize and determine behavior. Although no single set of assumptions governs the work of theorists such as Hawkins, Eisenberg, Tobach, Vygotsky, to name but a few writers who have influenced my own views, it is possible to formulate three assumptions which they do share. The choice of these notions is governed by their relevance to educational theory and practices and by the

139

fact that they offer an alternative view of human nature to that proposed by the sociobiologists.

The *first* of these is the view of human beings actively shaping and being shaped by their environment. Endler and Magnusson describe this assumption in their introduction to *Interactional Psychology and Personality*: "The person is an intentional and active agent in the interactional process. He interprets the situations and assigns meaning to them. To some extent, he selects his situational encounters and by his conscious and unconscious actions affects the character of the situations".[6] Earlier in this century both John Dewey and L. S. Vygotsky emphasized the active nature of human beings, and how this quality contributes to the construction of culture in the human species. Vygotsky, in particular, viewed humans as born into historically and culturally shifting contexts which they, too, eventually come to change.[7]

A *second* important assumption deals with the consequences of children's prolonged dependence upon their caretakers. Leon Eisenberg characterizes this dependence as providing "both an unparalleled opportunity for mental and emotional development and a period of vulnerability to profound distortion and neglect."[1] The implications of this human condition of dependence are far-reaching: it is the biological need for survival which creates, paradoxically, the opportunities for the culturally patterned socialization of the child.

A *third* assumption centers on the processes of learning. Within the interactionist paradigm learning is conceived as active and interactive: it cannot be reduced to the shaping of random responses through reinforcement nor to a maturationally-paced process. In the course of the sustained endeavors of young children, the young teach their elders to learn with them. Language is thus acquired: the mere exposure of a child to language on television is not sufficient for its acquisition. Instead, it requires reciprocal exchanges between speakers. Recent research has shown that adults, and even 4-year-old children, systematically modify their speech when they address toddlers learning to talk.[8]

The study of language acquisition has long served as the focus of competing theories and interpretations. Although recent research clearly supports the kind of interactionist assumptions presented above, many researchers still prefer to approach this subject by relying upon nativist concepts. Recently, J. B. Biggs proposed a sociobiological interpretation of the rapidity with which language is acquired by young children. He writes: "Oral language is obviously well toward the prepared end of the continuum: the mother tongue is acquired with astonishing rapidity by all but the severely handicapped. *Reading* and *writing*, as opposed to *speaking* the mother tongue appear further toward the unprepared end. In evolutionary terms this makes sense: Man has been speaking, as far as we can tell, for probably one million years, but has been writing for less than one percent of that time."[9]

If one were to take Biggs' argument seriously, it would be hard to interpret why in some countries (for instance, China or Cuba) universal literacy has been achieved in one generation, while in neighboring countries illiteracy is still very high. Does this mean that citizens in these differing nations represent different levels of "organismic preparedness" for reading and writing? Or is there a more reasonable explanation, namely, that in some countries literacy is a very high national priority.

The fact of individual and community-wide variations in the rate of learning need not be explained by a reliance upon genetic causes. A more promising approach lies in the careful examination of the historical and cultural factors which shape many aspects of human learning. A psychological theory which includes a strong reliance upon these dimensions offers the most rational approach to the understanding of individual and group differences.

In our own work[10] in Southwestern Indian communities we have come to recognize the challenge and the promise of cognitive diversity among growing children. For instance, the visual learning processes which are central to the development of Navajo and Pueblo children may play a less focal role in the life of urban learners, but nevertheless offer valuable lessons.

In the isolated sheep herding communities of the Navajo there is a lot of work to be done, particularly during the summers. Six-year-old children frequently herd sheep by themselves and thus spend long hours alone. Theirs is a responsible job which requires that they pay close attention to their environment. They study the quickly changing sky, the varied cloud formations; they pay attention to the directions of the wind. These are signals which they need to interpret—to assign meaning to—because if the weather changes quickly—and it frequently does in the West—the sheep will need to be protected; in a rapid downpour young lambs can get easily lost and some of them may even drown.

After several summers of participating in these family activities, including the lonely but challenging job of sheep-herding, the young Navajo child develops many skills in orienting to and interpreting the visual aspects of his or her environment. These young sheep-herders become visual thinkers. At the same time, as they have spent long stretches of time without anybody to talk to, they are frequently verbally shy when confronted with a large classroom of children, many of whom have spent all their young lives in the company of other people.

These functional differences in learning skills and learning styles are interpreted by some as genetically caused. However, the close working knowledge of the experiences of children raised in varied cultural environments leads to a different conclusion. An interactionist approach analyzes the settings into which children are born; how adults in a particular community sort, group and classify experience—what attributes of the environment they pay attention to and select to deal with, and for what reasons or uses they do so. Such an analysis is crucial, as the organization of children's learning is formed within specific socio-cultural contexts.

But schools frequently ignore what the child knows and has been learning at home: The young Navajo child is frequently flooded with English upon entering school—a language s/he knows poorly, if at all—and a reliance upon a verbal approach to teaching is a mistake for such children even if they are already bilingual. In addition, many reservation teachers interpret the children's quiet ways as a reflection of some intellectual limitation, instead of viewing such behavior as a different style of learning from that which they are used to in urban schools.

The difficulty most minority children face was described by the Harvard educator R. Edmonds, who criticized most schools as not "understanding, accepting and responding to the variety of cultures pupils represent".[11] One of the many reasons that teachers find it difficult to match their teaching methods to the learning strategies children bring to school is the following: most human beings rely upon a method of processing and expressing information which they developed during their own formal and informal education. This general human tendency is worse in the case of the education of minority children in the elementary schools, and of women in higher education: racist and sexist attitudes contribute to an attitude of blaming the victim. Cognitive diversity and a corresponding difference between the learners' own ways of approaching material and the teachers' methods is interpreted by those in authority as evidence of lower levels of learning potential on the part of the low-status student.

A belief in theories of genetic determinism, for instance, Jensen's concepts of Level I (memory) and Level II (reasoning) abilities,[12] contributes to inflexibility in teaching and failure to respond to children's culturally-patterned approaches. Thus, the inability of many educators to effectively modify their approaches in situations of cultural and social diversity is further worsened by the excuses implicit in hereditarian theories. In this way, theories of genetic destiny affect even some of the most caring teachers as they are unable to view learning as a dynamic and modifiable process. They fail to see that sex and group differences are better explained by prevalent socialization practices than by a reliance upon genetic causation.

The alternative view, as presented in this short paper, is espoused by those who see human diversity as socially shaped and culturally enriched. The historical and developmental interweaving of "Nature" and "Culture" is powerfully evoked by L. S. Vygotsky[7] within psychology; Leacock and Tobach use a related framework of "levels of organization and integration"[4] to free them of biological reductionism in the social sciences. These concepts help us to go beyond the necessary criticism of hereditarian theories to a more intriguing discussion of powerful, alternative models of thought about "the nature of human nature."

While my focus has been the education of minority children, and how certain widely-held beliefs restrict their opportunities to learn, I do not see this issue as separate from those raised by the other participants of this and previous conferences on Genes and Gender. The conceptual framework of many social scientists, the prevalence of hereditarian beliefs about the educability of women, Native Americans, Hispanics, Blacks, Asian-Americans are all interconnected. Such a framework has contributed to a one-sided research enterprise and to limited theory construction in the social and human sciences. Consequently, they have adversely affected all those who do not benefit from existing social arrangements. The real challenge is to expand further the interactionist and dialectical views of human development and social organization, which can effectively support the work of those who are committed, as has been said by E. W. Gordon, to "human diversity with social justice."[13]

REFERENCES

1   Eisenberg, L. The 'Human' Nature of Human Nature, *Science*, 176, April 14, 1972.
2   Gould, S. J. Biological Potential vs. Biological Determinism, in Caplan, A., *The Sociobiology Debate*, Harper and Row, New York, p. 349, 1978.
3   Quinton, A. Biology, Human Nature, and Ethical Theory, in Caplan, A., *The Sociobiological Debate*, Harper and Row, New York, p. 135. 1978.
4   Tobach, E. The Methodology of Sociobiology from the Point of View of a Comparative Psychologist, in Caplan, A., *The Sociobiological Debate*, Harper and Row, New York, pp. 411–424. 1978.
5   Hawkins, D., in *The Science and Ethics of Equality*, Basic Books, New York. 1977.
6   Endler, N. S. and Magnusson, D., in *Interactional Psychology and Personality*, John Wiley & Sons, New York. 1976.
7   Vygotsky, L. S., in *Mind in Society*, Harvard University Press, Cambridge, Mass. 1978.
8   Berko-Gleason, J. and Weintraub, S. Input Language and the Acquisition of Communicative Competence, in Nelson, K. *Children's Language*, Volume 1, Gardner Press, New York, 1978.
9   Biggs, J. B. Genetics and Education: An Alternative to Jensenism, in *The Educational Researcher*, April 1978.
10 John-Steiner, V. and Osterreich, H. *Learning Styles among Pueblo Children*, NIE Research Grant, Final Report, Albuquerque: University of New Mexico, Department of Educational Foundations, October, 1975.
11 Edmonds, R. "A Discussion of the Literature and Issues Related to Effective Schooling," Paper prepared for National Conference on Urban Education, CEMREL, Inc., St. Louis, Missouri, July, 1978.
12 Jensen, A. R. *Educability and Group Differences*, Harper and Row, New York, 1973.
13 Gordon, E. W. Toward a Conceptualization of Urban Education. *IRCD Bulletin*: Columbia University, New York, 3, No. 3, 1978.

CHILD BECOMES A PARENT

FOR MARGE
Phyllis Witte

This is the hardest poem
I have to write.
It concerns Twinkies and Cheerios.

When my sister and I were living
at home, once
my mother refused to let my sister touch
a package of Twinkie cupcakes
lying on the kitchen table.
My mother said, "Leave them alone,
they're for your sister."

I liked Twinkie cupcakes when I was little,
I liked Cheerios cereal too.
I would walk around the house eating
the cereal right out of the box.

My sister was skinny, for awhile, growing up.
I was chubby, for awhile, growing up.

Today, when I visit my sister, sometimes
I bring her a package of Twinkies.
I say to her, "Here, I found something
in my closet from a long time ago
that belongs to you, and somehow
I've gotten it."
Sometimes my sister serves me a box of
Cheerios with my tea.
Sometimes we laugh.
Sometimes we don't.

We know that it is not a question of
Twinkie cupcakes or Cheerios cereal.
It is a question of the time our mother
could not spend with us,
the problems she did not talk about,
the explanations she did not give,
the love she tried to give,
and needed to keep for herself too.

My sister and I give each other
cupcakes and cereal.
This is the hardest poem I have to write.

TEENAGE PREGNANCY
AND THE SEXIST IMAGE

Margaret Browne

Educational Testing Service

This paper will discuss the growing problem of teenage pregnancy and how the sexist image of women promoted by the media contributes to this "epidemic."

The health literature contains many studies which document the existence of what some investigators call the teenage pregnancy epidemic. Some of the findings are startling as the following examples show.

> Between 1940 and 1968 the illegitimacy rates for 15 to 19 year olds increased two to three fold.[1]
>
> In 1976, the illegitimacy rate for teenagers aged 15–19 declined for the first time since 1962. The decrease was a reflection of a decrease for black women, since the rate for white teenagers increased. (Rate for white teenagers increased 2%, while the rate for black teenagers decreased 4%).[2]
>
> In 1976, approximately one-third of the total of 988,267 legal abortions were obtained by teenage women.[3]
>
> Women less than 15 years old, in 1976, had the highest ratio of legal abortion. More women under 15 obtained abortions than delivered children.[3]
>
> In 1974, teenagers accounted for 20% of the births in the United States.[4]
>
> In 1974, of the 4,078,300 females aged 15–19 estimated to be in need of contraceptive services, i.e., sexually active, but not pregnant or desiring to be-

come pregnant, only 38% were receiving such services: 24% from organized programs and 14% from
private physicians.[4]

Although females under age 15 have few babies
and low fertility rates, the number of births to this
age group rose steeply from 6,780 in 1960 to 12,529
in 1975, an 85% increase.[5]

The majority of teenagers seeking prenatal or
postpartum services have never used any form of
contraception.[6]

Numerous investigators have conducted research into the
causes of teenage pregnancy and childbearing. They have
found some of the contributing factors in teenage pregnancy
and childbearing to be: decreasing age of menarche combined
with becoming sexually active at earlier ages; failure to use
contraception or ineffective use of contraception; contraceptive technology which is poorly adapted to teenagers' needs;
inaccessibility of contraceptives; and lack of knowledge of
reproduction and contraception.

One of the more interesting viewpoints on the causes of
teenage pregnancy and childbearing was expressed by Lor-
raine Klerman. She wrote:

The . . . problem is the still-too-narrow view of the
role of women. As long as the media continue to
*suggest that the most meaningful role for a woman
is* mother and housewife, many girls will wish to
reach that pinnacle as soon as possible—and the
decline of the mean age of menarche to 12.8 years
for white girls and 12.5 for black girls has made it
possible at a very young age. But the young woman
who plans to become a physician is not going to
allow herself to become pregnant at 16. . . . Despite
the best efforts of the Women's Liberation Movement, however most women are not career-ori-
ented. *The joys of suburban domestic life are too
often and too glowingly pictured on television and
on the covers of women's magazines.* If this role con-

151

tinues to be glorified over all others and an inadequate educational system makes it impossible for poor and minority group girls to even aspire to careers, then adolescent girls can be expected to look forward to early marriage and motherhood. Counselors can lecture interminably to school-age girls about the need to delay marriage and children until other aspects of their lives are well established; but, if these alternatives are seen as merely stop-gap activities of no significance in themselves, then there is little incentive for such delay.[6]

I agree with Klerman when she says that the "media continue to suggest that the most meaningful role for a woman is mother and housewife" and "the joys of suburban domestic life."

Therefore, I shall describe some commercials and one daytime serial and present what I think are the messages they convey about the roles of women. Television is a goldmine of things which can be criticized; I have chosen those commercials and one program which, in my opinion, present the most idealized, glorified, yet sexist images of women.

I do not think that media images alone cause teenage pregnancy. But in combination with some of the other factors which I mentioned and some which I did not, media images are not without impact.

Birdseye International Vegetables

Scene: A man who is about fifty with a European accent, says: "This is a dish which my beautiful wife cooked for me . . . and your beautiful wife can cook for you." The commercial ends with a voiceover which says, "Birdseye International vegetables, you cook it over there, but it tastes like here." The "beautiful wife" in this commercial looks more like the man's daughter; she resembles a twenty year old Sophia Loren.

Message:
1. Youth and beauty determine the value of women.
2. Men value women in terms of their ability to please them:

152

"a dish which my . . . wife cooked for me."

The following is the current version of the same commercial which now appears on television.

Scene: A man whose working class background is indicated by his accent says: "My wife, Angela. I met her in Italy. She's smart and can she cook." Angela enters with a bowl of vegetables. While the man continues to extol her cooking, she stands behind him, shakes her head in the negative, and pantomimes, "Birdseye."

Messages:

1. Women are valued in terms of their success in pleasing men.

2. A not exactly implicit message is that the husband married Angela for her cooking. Therefore, the traditional housewifely role is of prime importance in marriage.

3. The kitchen is female or specifically wifely territory, and responsibility for meal preparation is that of females. After all, while Angela was preparing the meal, didn't the husband go into the kitchen for anything? If he had, surely he would have seen that she simply opened a box of frozen vegetables.

4. Women must be devious and furtive. This is how powerless people maneuver in situations in which they have no control. This reinforces the age old myths of feminine mystery and deception.

Stovetop Stuffing

These commercials feature real consumers, not actors. A wife is asked which side dish her husband would choose to eat with chicken—mashed potatoes or stuffing. Always the husband chooses Stovetop Stuffing. After this revelation, the wife shows surprise and says that in the future, she will serve Stovetop Stuffing. A picture of the husband is projected on the screen; and a voiceover says: "To please your family, serve Stovetop Stuffing instead of mashed potatoes."

Messages:

1. Again, pleasing men. In this commercial, pleasing the family is defined as pleasing a man (husband).

Apparently, Madison Avenue has found this type of commercial profitable; for there are now spinoffs: White Cloud toilet tissue, Clorox bleach, and Good Seasons salad dressing. In one of the White Cloud commercials, after the husband has chosen that brand of tissue and said that softness is important to him, the wife says that she will buy White Cloud because "it's a very small thing to do to keep him happy."

In these and other commercials, women are rarely depicted as workers. This contradicts present day reality: women now constitute about 49% of the labor force in the United States, and this percentage is predicted to increase.

When women are presented as members of the labor force, they are shown in occupations in which women actually make up a very small percentage of the work force. Women are pictured as jockeys in the Shasta diet soda and Carnation Instant Breakfast commercials. In the Stouffer's frozen food and Prell shampoo commercials, women are shown as successful professionals. Again, this does not square with reality: about 90% of working women are employed in low-level clerical, service, and sales jobs.

Television daytime programming is lucrative. Last year on NBC alone, daytime programming produced advertising sales of $225 million dollars. 5.5 million households comprised NBC's daytime viewing audience. NBC lags behind CBS and ABC in ratings and revenue; therefore, the combined daytime advertising sales amount to billions of dollars. Tens of millions of viewers must watch the daytime programs of the three major networks.

I shall discuss the characterization of women in one of the most popular daytime serials.

The Young and the Restless

This daytime serial may be called the soap opera of the beautiful people. Most of the women are young and very pretty. The men are equally handsome and of leading man quality. Sustained close-up of all of these beautiful and handsome faces is the most frequently used camera technique. Let us look at some of the female characters in this program.

Leslie Brooks Prentice: Concert pianist, beautiful and

154

wealthy. She is pregnant with a child whose father is her sister Laurie's husband. But when Leslie found out that she was pregnant as a result of what actually amounted to a romanticized one night stand, she never considered the option of abortion. She decided to go on an extended concert tour. But, man to the rescue! Her lover's brother offers to marry her after he discovers her pregnancy and the circumstances of the conception. They marry and some more obvious problems are solved.

Message:

1. A woman should always want to carry a baby to term regardless of the circumstances of conception or the personal or social consequences of giving birth.

2. There will always be a man who will eventually come to your rescue.

Laurie Brooks Prentice: Before she married, an unhappy, discontented, unfulfilled woman driven by her jealousy of Leslie. But voila! Laurie is transformed into a happy, contented, fulfilled woman after she marries Lance Prentice, a handsome, wealthy man with apparently worldwide business interests, who makes intercontinental trips in his private jet.

Jill Foster: Of a working class background. Her father deserted the family, two sons and Jill, when they were young children. The mother supported the family by working in a factory. However, one son becomes a doctor and the other a lawyer. Did Jill rise above these circumstances? Certainly not! She works as a hairdresser. Later she becomes the hired companion of rich Catherine Chancellor. She falls in love with Mrs. Chancellor's husband, Phillip, has an affair with him, and of course gets pregnant. Phillip, who does not love his wife, proposes marriage to Jill because he does love her; and she is pregnant with his child. However, before Phillip can make Jill's Cinderella story a reality, he dies from injuries received in a traffic accident.

Jill gets another job as a hairdresser and meets Derek Thurston and falls in love with him. But Catherine Chancellor is again the foil: she tricks Derek into marrying her. Next, Jill sets out to marry Stuart Brooks, wealthy owner of the local newspaper and father of Leslie and Laurie. Jill uses sex to entice and lure Stuart. In order to coerce him into marrying, she lies to him about being pregnant with his child. And of course, Stuart does the noble thing: he proposes marriage to Jill.

Catherine Chancellor: Rich, of the local ruling class. She is economically independent and secure, educated, and powerful. However, her life is empty and lonely; she drinks and smokes rather excessively. Apparently, the only thing that can change her is a man. Therefore, she insists on holding on to a husband who does not love her (her deceased first husband, Phillip); and she tricks a man who does not love her (Derek) into marriage.

Mom Foster: Salt of the earth. Mother of Jill, Greg (lawyer), and Snapper (doctor). She supported her family by working in a facotry after her husband deserted the family; many years later she is reunited with him. Mom Foster's life must have been hard as any working class woman who has been the sole economic support of a family knows. Yet she is the opposite of Catherine Chancellor: Mom Foster is serenely resigned to her life.

The Young and the Restless is a slickly produced package of daytime serial stereotypes and trite plots. However, these characters and plots can be found with some slight variation in all other daytime serials.

These are the universal messages conveyed by daytime serials:

1. To marry is the only goal to which women should aspire. The achievement of this goal solves all problems, personal, social, and economic.

2. To bear a child is one of the principal means by which goal #1 can be attained.

3. Woman's place is in the home; therefore, her role, interests, and concerns should be home centered.

4. Children, regardless of the circumstances of conception, will always be wanted by those who conceived them.

5. To provide and maintain an optimum quality of life for children is easy.

6. Do not take responsibility for your sexual activity. If you watch daytime serials, have you ever noticed that pregnancy seems to always follow coitus? The use of contraception is non-existent.

7. You will be punished if you have an abortion. Women in daytime serials rarely choose to terminate pregnancy. However, whenever they do, they are punished by either sterility, infertility, loss of husband or boyfriend, alienation of family, or extreme emotional trauma.

8. Political, social, and economic conditions exert no influence on the lives of people. Daytime serial characters seem to live in plastic capsules of oblivion.

In this International Year of the Child what must we do for our teenage children who are sexually active and may bear children? I am referring to boys as well as girls for if you will, boys *and* girls, get pregnant.[7]

The Alan Guttmacher Institute has suggested a national program to cope with the teenage pregnancy epidemic. It includes:

1. Realistic sex education through schools, churches, youth agencies and the media.

2. An expanded network of preventive family planning programs and adequate pregnancy counseling services.

3. Equal availability and accessibility of legal abortion to all women regardless of their income, where they live or other factors.

4. Adequate medical care—before, during and after pregnancy—for those who choose to have their babies.

5. Educational, employment and social services for adolescent parents and day care facilities for their children.

6. Greater research to discover safe and effective birth control techniques that fill the needs of young people.

However, a program which focuses only on teenage pregnancy is not enough. Educational and career opportunities for youth, particularly minority and white working class youth, must be expanded. As these opportunities increase, young boys and girls may consider the timing and values of teenage childbearing against the available economic, educational and social realities.

157

Educational and career opportunities for our children will increase only if we fight against the racism, sexism, and classism which limit, restrict, and even destroy these opportunities. [8] It is imperative that we wage this fight now because our elected officials have neither the commitment nor the will to do so.

REFERENCES

1 Hinman, A. R., Stroh, G., Gesche, M. and Whitaker, K., Medical consequences of Teenage Sexuality. *New York State Journal of Medicine*, pp. 1439–42, August, 1975.

2 U.S. Department of Health, Education, and Welfare, *Monthly Vital Statistics Report, Advance Report, Final Natality Statistics*, the National Center for Health Statistics, 1976.

3 Center for Disease Control, *Abortion Surveillance Summary United States, 1976*, Washington, D.C.: United States Government Printing Office, 1978.

4 U.S. Department of Health, Education and Welfare Center for Disease Control: *Teenage Fertility in the United States: 1960, 1970, 1974 Regional and State Variation and Excess Fertility*, 1978.

5 Center for Disease Control: *Abortion Surveillance Summary United States, 1974*, 1976.

6 Klerman, L. V., Adolescent Pregnancy: The Need for New Policies and New Programs, *The Journal of School Health*, XLV, No. 5, 264, 1975.

7 Lucker, K., in *Taking Chances: Abortion and the Decision Not to Contracept*. Berkeley: University of California Press, 1975.

8 *The Bakke Case: The Myth of Reverse Racism Revisited*, International Committee Against Racism, New York, 1977.

PSYCHIATRIC RISK AND GENDER: THE VULNERABLE CHILD

Doris Bartlett

Our experience in life is that we change. As therapists, working with families, couples or individuals, we participate in and observe change. Some of the most profound conflicts and changes we observe today are the experiences and feelings that women and men are struggling with in relation to one another and to themselves. Changes are occurring in the traditional roles and in the assumptions about power and powerlessness. In the course of therapy also, changes occur in the enclosed family system of fixed roles and begin to affect the consciousness and attitudes of all family members.

In certain times of stress, this kind of integration of activities and beliefs happens in family members without benefit of professional therapists. Witness West Virginia Harlan County families in the midst of a coal strike. The extraordinary changes that took place between women and men, women and women, parents and children, rapidly moved women from vulnerable, passive, auxiliary and inactive positions to unusual cooperation with men and with one another; they moved to positions of leadership, to action and creative initiative for a common economic need and goal.

Social struggles and class struggles such as the women's movement and the Harlan County strike are ways in which people change in their relationships to one another and to the rest of society. Psychotherapists frequently are involved in such struggles for change. However, there always seems to be a reaction to change brought about in that way—and too often scientific argument and research are used to bolster that

160

reaction; science itself becomes part of that reaction.

I do believe that scientific vision can be blurred by the underlying beliefs that determine scientific research. For example, some psychiatrists, psychologists and other researchers in mental health have believed, and do believe, that the "vulnerabilities" of the girl are genetically determined. For some, belief in woman's "natural" passivity and man's dominance is comfortable because it "fits" with the economic-social milieu and existing relationships. It must be acknowledged that in the field of psychology, many investigations and conclusions about girls and women reflect a status-quo mentality, based on the appearance of what seems natural, and therefore, appropriate—thus normal and enduring. if a psychologist views passivity, obedience and submissiveness as femaleness, then there is little need for concern, alarm or change when a girl is passive. After all, it was not too many years ago that the ideal woman was one who was dainty, helpless, could not tolerate the vulgar aspects of life, fainted easily, "suffered" the sexual demands of her husband and had "mysterious" womanly ailments. She was not supposed to be vigorous and she was supposed to be closer to saintliness than men. (Of course this did not include working class women or Black women.) In Europe this middle-class Victorian woman was the basis for Freud's psychoanalytic theory about women.

A similar view of the unchangingness of human beings and the "naturalness" of women's passivity and submissiveness is apparent in the writings of ethologists, and the many psychologists and anthropologists who were strongly influenced by them. Lorenz, Tiger et al. created an image of the modern person as a "naked ape" living in a "human zoo". Evolutionary developments, they argued, and claimed to demonstrate, resulted in the male instinct for aggression, for hierarchical behavior and for dominance.[1] Women, they claimed, were genetically well-endowed for sexual response to men and care of children, but ill-endowed for forming groups. In this view, people are living unhappily in a technologic world because they are still driven by biological programming for territoriality, aggression and dominance in men and for nesting, nurturing and dependent attachments in women. In modern life these drives are frustrated, thus leading to mental illness and all kinds of problems. This is one view of the unchangingness of human life, of gender roles and of human history.

Moving from this distorted view to a more recently advertised version we are confronted with a molecular biology (genetics) and neurophysiology that emerges as sociobiology.[2] This view attempts to enclose even more of human history in the human genes. We are told that there exists a genetic basis for making rules, for altruism and, of course, for gender-appropriate behavior. There also exists a physiological source for human optimism and depression. Tiger[3] says that our "benign sense of the future could have been bred into us and other complex animals out of the need to survive." He says that we may be programmed for hope—just as we are genetically endowed for depression. Depression is good for the human species, he says, because depression slows down action and this has an advantage to the community. People who are depressed can function as a conservative force. Genes for depression therefore are helpful in preventing too rapid social change. We would have to assume from this that since it is mainly women who suffer depression, it has the benign effect of inhibiting their own change in order not to upset the *status-quo* too much!

One geneticist holds that the answer to pathological behavior in children will be found in the study of genes and biochemistry.[4] Eventually, control of abnormal behavior will be through the manipulation of the genes or appropriate chemicals. He is convinced that the vulnerable child, in psychiatric terms, will be modified by the application of behavioral genetics. One must learn about the "genetic loci" influencing behavior. He says, "some genes control personality—other genes—the color of one's eyes or the length of one's toes". One of the difficulties with this is that there is no statement as to what is considered normal. The implication must be that it is that which is socially acceptable—but what is socially acceptable is certainly in a state of flux at all times. As we have seen, biograms have been argued for gender-roles; now personality itself is biogrammed.

A parallel view of human nature is central to classical psychoanalysis. Women in particular are doomed by their "innate" masochism and their "anatomy as destiny." They are supposed to perceive themselves as incomplete men because of the absence of a penis. This results in penis envy and a need to threaten men with castration. The girl-child eventually adjusts to the discovery of "no penis." She overcomes her shock at this "mutilation" and adapts herself to the "need" for mothering and nurturing.[5] The psychoanalytic view also relies heavily on instincts, biology and physiology to explain what takes place in human relationships.

I will not elaborate on the astounding ways that psychoanalytic theory has distorted women's social experience and history in the patriarchal family relationships. Much sharp and illuminating criticism has already been written, but the core of this view of the sources of gender-identity for women is still maintained. For example, one psychoanalyst revising Freud's theory, has it that civilization is built on the basis of men's fear of women; it is their defense against their castration fear that causes men to develop the means by which to dominate women. As a result women come to consider themselves inferior and maimed creatures. In this version of the theory, women define themselves as incomplete men, not because they actually are (according to the old version) but because "by structuring itself according to the male castration complex, civilization sets the conditions upon which women are forced to define themselves as castrated."[6] We have here a convoluted effort to include social processes in the psychology of women, but we still end up with civilization as the product of masculine instincts.

I do believe that in psychology and related fields there has been a search for something "basic," which often means biological or genetic, that would explain the differences in attitudes and psychological states of women and men. For Jung it appeared to be the *animus,* the masculine component that exists for both sexes but which women are supposed somehow to incorporate successfully without its interfering with their "biological tasks".[5] In much of psychological measurements, the search centered on the concept of traits and derived degrees of masculinity and femininity. Persistently, the measurements demonstrated and gave "evidence" that the neurotic woman unconsciously desired to be masculine and the healthy woman accepted her innate need to nurture and possessed all the qualities of tender emotions and an absence of aggressiveness, boldness, etc. The Minnesota Multiphasic Inventory is one of the typical psychological measurements that differentiates on a masculinity and femininity scale and is still widely used in hospitals, schools and clinics.

Even in research on therapist-bias about gender-roles, one psychologist[7] says that it is unfair to blame Freudian psychoanalytic theory for perpetuating traditionalism or sexism in gender definitions or roles. She says that our attitudes are what they are and such criticism may simply reflect our own projections or a lack of a thorough psychoanalysis. She points to the fact that Freudian theory and practice urges women to realize their "masculine" potential by "thrusting" self-achievement and accomplishment. It is ironic that in the very effort to investigate stereotypic thinking about gender-identity, achievements and self-assertion are defined as masculine.

Some psychologists get enmeshed in a strange reasoning when they attempt to acknowledge that society, culture, and economics have something to do with gender-identity and roles. In the very attempt to recognize some connections, the warning is given that as psychotherapists "we must never forget that cultural wrongs are separate from psychological determinism and growth". Growth, in this theory, is defined as the psychosexual stages which psychoanalytic theory consider biologically determined.[8]

Some twenty-five years ago, a significant leap took place from work with an individual psyche to work with the interpersonal and situational factors of a family group. Family therapy emerged because many mental health workers began to recognize that the connections between individuals with psychological problems and their families could be studied directly. The de-emphasis of the concept of an isolated individual psyche evolving out of a struggle with instinctual behavior gave promise of an approach to understanding people, that is, how they form and change one another in their connectedness to all of society. This led to the examination of the family as a system and for some it led to an examination of the social milieu in which the family existed. Some sociologists became active partners with mental health workers in this new effort. This was progress. Family, socialization processes, class differences, oppressive social institutions—all came into question. But even with this progress, theories of genetic determinism and innate gender roles were maintained.

It should be noted that the field of sociology was influenced by psychoanalytic theory at that time. As a result, certain theories in sociology,[9] highly influential in the development of family therapy actually reinforced the original psychoanalytic and medical tendencies of this new field. For example, one sociological theory[10] is an elaboration of family relationships based on psychological differences often put in terms of lactating and non-lactating organisms. Many family therapists uncritically absorbed the view that the "biological" bond between mother and child eventually led to the woman carrying the "expressive" role, the emotional climate, in the integration of family relationships, while men carried the instrumental one of financial support and maneuvering this outer environment. That his was simply a description of the existing situation seemed to have escaped notice. It was assumed to be natural and inevitable for the modern family. Even Murray Bowen, a pioneer in the field of family therapy and research[11] and one who has put great emphasis on understanding families as operating systems, proposes that the emotional system of a family is part of the biologic forces that govern autonomic functions. The more life is governed by emotions, the more it follows the course of instinctual behavior. According to this formulation, women are more feeling, more emotional and therefore more instinctual and less cognitive, etc. So here again, when families are viewed as systems and thus supposedly not amenable to stereotyping, gender stereotypes creep in.

A blatant application of traditionalism, sexism and implied biologic determinism is found in an article dealing with the family and the effects of women's liberation on gender-identity.[12] (The author means the gender-identity of the male-child although that is not made clear at first.) He states that "only mothers can inculcate in young children . . . the meaning and abiding sense of basic and familial social values." Gender identity, he argues, is best established in the traditional (patriarchal) family structure, because that structure legitimizes masculine assertion essential for the formation of heterosexual love. Women who choose to work, who insist on equal marital authority are harming the gender-identity and psycho-sexual development of the male child. In this argument the traditional functions of women are considered "natural" and necessary to the normal growth of boys. Although this article can be considered a caricature of the role of women in the family, it does, even within the new field of family therapy, indicate how strong the reaction can be to social change.

What is the significance of the evidence presented? In this year of the child, girl-children are still in danger of *not* growing up as fully productive members of this society. The social changes have not yet been made that allow for her full development. The passage of the equal rights amendment will not provide in itself for a girl-child's blossoming into a healthy, fully responsible and conscious adult. We have to be alert to the theories and practices that deter or support the changes that will promote growth.

The formulation of gender-identity and "human nature" described above not only give credence to prejudice and stereotypic thinking but by-pass human history. This insistence, whether by ethologists, socio-biologists or psychoanalysts that our nature is somehow locked and predetermined by our genes ignores the *history of humans making themselves human*. Our history is a social process involving enormous diversity of activities and modes of living, of beliefs and attitudes that have changed over time. To ignore those activities and diversity which keep emerging as changing human consciousness is to minimize and devalue human history and our consciousness of it. To ignore change and attempt to bring us back to so-called "basics" and "natural" states only contributes to the misunderstanding of the social, economic and cultural sources of gender-identity. It also hides the need and effort to change the social relationships that are not beneficial to people. A "science" that keeps maintaining that what *appears*

166

to be natural will always be "natural", is not scientific; science teaches us that it is change that is natural. The search for a "basic human nature" to explain gender identity, altruism, aggression or dominance only leads us away from understanding the actual relationships that do form us.

One such problem is that the mental health of girl-children is precarious. Psychiatric risk, meaning vulnerability to stress of various kinds, resulting in clinical disorders, is greater for girls. When the child cannot integrate *who* she/he is with *what* she/he is; when the child cannot adequately process and order information to be able to act; when stress threatens the child's security with resulting feelings of victimization and passivity; when there is a lack of balance in the environment between stress and psychological supports; and when there is a lack of harmony between the "internal" and external environments, a risk exists that health will be damaged.[13]

Researchers have found girls to be less competent to handle stress than boys; this may be due to the fact that girls tend to become frozen and immobilized in stress situations, less able to act and accommodate to change.[14] Girls are less satisfied with being who they are, less able to confront the world with what they want for themselves. They are less autonomous and have less self-esteem. The deficiencies in autonomy and self-esteem are passed on from generation to generation through the *process of gender identification*; not through the genes: the lack of support from others is evident in that parents seem to prefer boys and that teachers pay more direct attention to boys.[15] Sociologists and anthropologists over the years have given us other evidence that children are *inducted* into gender-identity. The functions of girls, boys, women, men are determined by the particular society in which they grow up.

In our society such induction has been demonstrated by many studies of child development.[16] For example, Beverly Birns has reviewed more than 25 studies of cognition, play, parent-infant interactions, field dependence and adult perceptions of baby behavior when the sex of the baby was not known. A few of her findings were that neonate boys may be bigger than girls but not necessarily more alert, responsive or aggressive; that adults will perceive certain behavior in a baby

167

and label it feminine or masculine depending on what they *assume* is the child's gender. If adults believe that an infant crying is a boy then they are more likely to assume "he" is angry; if they think the child is a girl they assume "she" is fearful. Between the ages of 24 to 36 months there are no sex differences in cognitive styles but by 3 to 5 years there are differences; boys are more exploratory and aggressive and girls are more sedentary. Birns concludes that differences between girls and boys can be considered due to learning inside and outside the family. Gender identity and roles are taught and fostered by the activities of adults with stereotyped beliefs and abilities with girls and boys.

Family therapists have ample opportunity to observe such indoctrination and exercises of such beliefs. We watch fathers insist on defining "femininity" for girls and mothers blamed for the absence or over-abundance of these qualities. We observe terrible struggles arising out of the insisting on traditional roles and functions when they are no longer real or necessary. A woman or adolescent girl may be working and contributing to family finances; in reality she is not dependent on the husband or father, but she is expected to *act* as though she were. We become directly aware of how the myths of "innate" femininity are perpetuated. At the same time we observe the painful, confusing efforts of family members to change; the efforts of mothers and fathers to share in child-rearing; of husbands and wives struggling for more egalitarian relationships with one another; of girls striving to assert their competencies and brothers trying to avoid and correct their stereotypic responses to sisters. We also observe mothers attempting to relinquish being the ultimate source of nurture in the family.

It is astounding, or perhaps all too predictable, that in this decade of upheaval and change in the relations of women to men and to society, so much re-emerges in science to counteract that change. We need science to help us out of the confusions—not to push us back. We need to know and understand what socializing methods are best for the developing child . . . what are the necessary conditions for that? How do we create the balance between stress and support, between vulnerabilities and strengths for girls and boys in our society? Perhaps even more important: how can science best study progressive change so that we can accelerate desirable change?

This paper has two main points: that prejudice in science exists and persists and that, particularly significant, is the investigation of gender-roles and gender psychology. The second point is that gender roles are taught and are historically determined. Therefore, they change according to the need, progression or decay of a particular society at a particular period in history.

A third point is that science itself has a history that cannot be separated from the social milieu in which it eixsts. Although some significant investigations now take into account the researcher as a variable, too few acknowledge this. Too few scientists take responsibility for how information will be put to use. Given the present social and economic situation, scientific information is directly utilized to justify political policies. We cannot rely any longer on the comforting concept of scientific objectivity; science that is used to sanction policies that harm us is not a dependable science. We have seen this in the misuse of nuclear energy for bombs and in industrial plants that have harmed many people.

The implication for all of us, and particularly for psychotherapists, is that how we define health (physical and mental) depends on our world-view, on what we consider important in life. The level of our own consciousness, of our participation in society is critical. In the case of gender identity and gender role, psychologists' *social* theory may well determine their scientific theory.

REFERENCES

1 Bartlett, D. and Bartlett, F., Biological Determinism. *Science & Society*, New York, 135, pp. 209–219, 1971.

2 Wilson, E. O. in *On Human Nature*, Harvard Univ. Press, Cambridge, Mass., 1978. *Sociobiology*, Harvard Univ. Press, Cambridge, Mass., 1975.

3 Tiger, Lionel, in *Optimism, The Biology of Hope*, Simon-Schuster, New York, 1979.

4 Rosenberg, Leon, in *A Geneticist's Approach to the Vulnerable Child in His Family.* Anthony & Koupernik (eds.), Wiley, New York, 1974.

5 Miller, J. B. in *Psychoanalysis & Women*, Brunner/Mazel, New York, 1973.

6 Kovel, Jose. The Castration Complex Reconsidered, in *Women & Analysis*, J. Strouse (ed.), Dell, New York, 1975.

7 Steinman, Anne. Cultural Values, Female Role Expectations and Therapeutic Goals. in *Women in Therapy*, Franks, V. & Burtle, V. (eds.), Brunner/Mazel, New York, 1974.

8 Fenshel, G., *Issues in Ego Psychology*, Vol. 1, Washington Square Institute for Psychotherapy and Mental Health, New York, 1975.

9 Parsons, T. and Bales, R. F. in *Family Socialization and Interaction*, Free Press, New York, 1955.

10 Bell, J. and Vogel, T. in *A Modern Introduction to the Family*, Free Press, New York, 1968.

11 Bowen, Murray. in *Family Therapy in Clinical Practice*, Prentice, New Jersey, 1978.

12 Levine, M. Women's Liberation—Its Effect on Family Stability and Gender Identity in Adults and Youth, *Israel Annals of Psychiatry and Related Disciplines*, 10. March, 1972.

13 Anthony, James. "The Syndrome of the Psychologically Vulnerable Child." in *The Child and His Family*, Anthony & Koupernik (eds.) Wiley, New York, 1974.

14 Murphy, Lois B. "The Problem of Defense and the Concept of Coping," in *The Child and His Family*, 1. 1970.

15 Birns, Beverly. "Emergence and Socialization of Sex Differences in Early Years," in *Annual Progress in Child Psychiatry and Development*, Chess, S. and Thomas, A. (eds.), Brunner/Mazel, New York, 1977.

16 *Women, Culture and Society*, Stanford University Press, Palo Alto, California, pp. 324–331, 1974.

BIOGRAPHICAL SKETCHES

Sophie Balk, M.D., is a full-time attending pediatrician at the Bronx Municipal Hospital Center and an instructor in pediatrics at the Albert Einstein College of Medicine. Before coming to the Bronx Municipal Hospital Center, she spent the two years from 1977–1979 working in a federally-funded group practice in East Harlem. She is a member of the International Committee Against Racism.

Doris Bartlett received her B.A. in 1945 and M.A. in 1946 from City College in New York City and completed doctoral studies at Teachers College, Columbia University in 1964. She is a Clinical Professor at New York University and was Chief Psychologist from 1974–1976 with the Jewish Family Service where she developed training programs for staff in clinical and group therapies and supervised and taught these programs. From 1971–1974 she was the Chief Psychologist at Gouverneur and Beth Israel Hospitals. At present, she is in private practice.

Margaret Browne works at the Educational Testing Service since 1979 where she is an assistant examiner in the health program. From 1977 to 1978 she was an instructor at Brooklyn College, New York, in the Basic Skills Program. From 1973 until 1977 she was an Adjunct Assistant Professor in the Biology Department at Pace University. She earned her B.S. in zoology at Knoxville College, Tennessee, an M.A. in Science Education at Teachers College, Columbia University and an M.Ed. in Health Education at Teachers College. Her main interest is in working with the International Committee Against Racism.

Dorothy C. Burnham, M.A., from Brooklyn College, in 1960; biologist; Assistant Professor at Empire State College of State University of New York; research on Black Women in slavery.

Linda Dudley (Lindamichellebaron) began writing as a junior high school student. She edited school journals and continued to write poetry. She has also appeared as a dramatic performer and toured in *Amen Corner* and *Dark Symphony* in which her poetry was featured. Her poems were included in *When Hell Freezes Over I'll Skate*. She has published such books as *Black is Beautiful* and *Going Through Changes*. She received a B.A. degree from New York University, an M.A. from Columbia University and is working on an M.B.A. at Hofstra University. She is presently working as a sales consultant with a major publishing house. She is committed to improving academic achievement of young people.

Mary June Bayuk Gelles graduated from Mt. Sinai Hospital School of Nursing in 1963. She received a B.S.N.E. from Teachers College, Columbia University. She has done nursing for many years at Mt. Sinai and Albert Einstein Hospitals in New York. She has also worked in New York City day-care centers and is at present a school nurse. She is working towards a Master's degree in nursing education at Teachers College, Columbia University. She is an active member of the International Committee Against Racism.

Edmund W. Gordon, Ed.D. in 1957 from Teachers College, Columbia University. At present he is Professor of Psychology, Afro-American Studies, Child Study Center, at Yale University. His major interests are education of low status populations; ethnic desegregation and integration in schools; human diversity, group and individual differences, in pedagogy; bias and alternatives strategies in psychological and educational testing; implications for schooling of differences in sex and gender; correlates of success and failure in disadvantaged populations. He is the author or co-author of *Compensatory Education: Pre-School Through College; Equal Educational Opportunity* and *Human Diversity and Pedagogy.* He is editor of the American Journal of Orthopsychiatry.

Vera P. John-Steiner received her B.A. in Psychology, Barnard, 1950; and her Ph.D. in Social and Developmental Psychology, University of Chicago, 1956. Her fields of specialization are psycholinguistics and cognitive psychology. She has taught at UCLA, University of Rochester, Yeshiva University, and the University of New Mexico. Among her publications are *Early Childhood Education* with Vivian Horner; *Mind in Society,* co-edited with Michael Cole, Sylvia Scribner, and Ellen Souberman; and *Functions of Language in the Classroom,* co-edited with Courtney Cazden and Dell Hymes. She teaches a course in the Psychology of Women and has published a number of articles in this area.

Iris Lopez is a doctoral candidate in anthropology at Columbia University studying women, fertility, and sterilization among Puerto Ricans. She earned her B.A. in anthropology and Latin American Literature at New York University and an M.A. degree from Columbia University in Caribbean Urban and Medical Anthropology. She has developed curricula for promoting affective and cognitive skills of students at Boricua College. She has recently been awarded a Whitney Young Jr. Foundation Fellowship.

Donna Lovell received her B.A. degree from City College of New York in 1976 in American History. She works in the Native American Education Program in New York City where she is a curriculum developer/historian concerning Native Americans. She has coordinated cultural exchange programs between Shinnecock children and Asian-American students. She has provided resource materials to various schools and institutions concerning Native Americans.

Diane Margo Morales received a B.A. from City College and an M.S.W. from Hunter College School of Social Work. She is on the District #3 School Board of New York City and is presently the Council Coordinator for the Mid-Westside Neighborhood Health Council, Inc./Neighborhood Health Services. She has been working to improve health and social conditions in New York City since 1967.

Leith Mullings, Ph.D. from Unversity of Chicago in anthropology, and B.S. in nursing from Cornell University; research on women, ethnicity, health and stratifications; Assistant Professor in Anthropology at Columbia University; member of Women for Racial and Economic Equality.

Helen Rodriguez-Trias, M.D., from the University of Puerto Rico in 1962. At present she is director of the Children and Youth Program at St. Luke's Roosevelt Hospital Center and Associate Clinical Professor at Columbia University College of Physicians and Surgeons. Her previous appointments were Director of Pediatrics at Lincoln Hospital, Associate Professor in Social Medicine at Montefiore and Associate Professor in Pediatrics at Albert Einstein College of Medicine. Her professional interests are teaching social pediatrics and developing programs to provide continuing care for inner city children. She is a founding member of the committee to End Sterilization Abuse, an organization involved in Patients' rights.

Betty Rosoff, Ph.D., from the City University of New York, in 1967; endocrinologist; Professor of Biology, Stern College of Yeshiva University. She is on the editorial board of a new journal, *The Prostate*. She applies her expertise in endocrinology to the scientifically valid investigation of gender and biological determinism.

Arthur Schatzkin, M.D., M.P.H., is an internist and Resident in General Preventive Medicine at Mount Sinai Medical Center in New York City. He is currently completing a doctorate in public health in the Division of Sociomedical Sciences at the Columbia University School of Public Health. His research interests include socioeconomic and racial differentials in the epidemic chronic diseases and racial segregation in U.S. urban medical care. He is a member of the International Committee Against Racism.

Ethel Tobach, Ph.D., from New York University, 1957, comparative psychologist in the Department of Animal Behavior, The American Museum of Natural History; research on the evolution and development of social-emotional behavior; has written on the role of science in societal processes leading to racism and sexism; faculty associate of the Center for the Study of Women and Sex Roles, Graduate Center, The City University of New York.

Georgine M. Vroman, Ph.D., Graduate Faculty, New School for Social Research, 1979; medical anthropologist. Primary and secondary education in Indonesia; medical studies at Rijks-University, Utrecht, Netherlands; has lived in the U.S. since 1947. Biomedical research 1947–1950, followed by a prolonged period of family care and volunteer community work. Returned to graduate studies in 1972, combining old and new interests. Special concerns: stroke/aphasia; urban issues; aging; the interface between biology and culture. At present holding adjunct position at Ramapo College, N.J.

Phyllis Witte is a New York City poet. She has read for: The New York Tribunal for Crimes Against Women, Columbia University, New York Radical Feminists, Queens College, Empire State College, Chumley's, Soho Books, Friends School in Brooklyn, The Museum of Natural History, Cornelia Street Cafe, Queensborough Community College, Art & Ice Cream, and The English Pub. Her poems have been published in The Denver Quarterly, City 6 Magazine of the City University in Manhattan, Pulp Magazine, The English Teacher, and Year at the Spring. She holds an A.A. degree from Queensborough Community College, and a B.A. from Empire State College; she is 26 years old.